EDDIE WOO'S MAGICAL MATHS 2

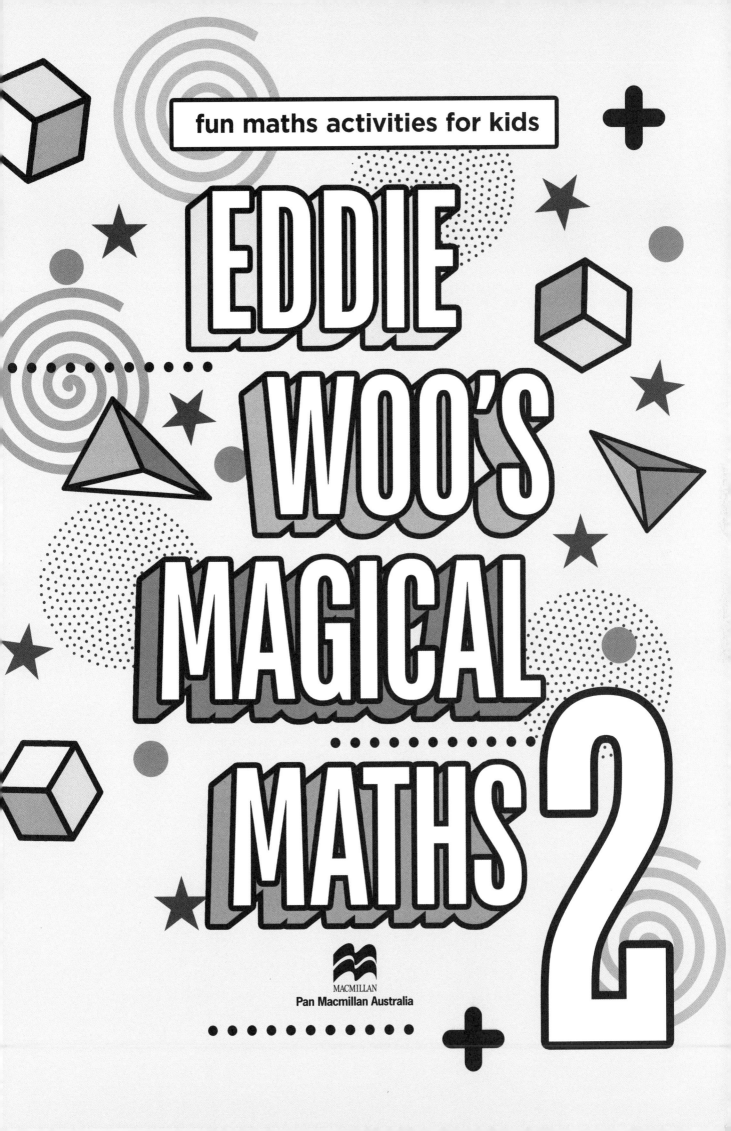

fun maths activities for kids

EDDIE WOO'S MAGICAL MATHS 2

MACMILLAN
Pan Macmillan Australia

First published 2020 in Macmillan by Pan Macmillan Australia Pty Ltd
1 Market Street, Sydney, New South Wales, Australia, 2000

 A catalogue record for this
book is available from the
National Library of Australia

Cover and text design by Alissa Dinallo
Illustrations by Alissa Dinallo
Images on pages 80-83, 85, 87, 102, 132 courtesy of Shutterstock.

Printed in China by Hang Tai Printing Co. Ltd

10 9 8 7 6 5 4 3 2

To my students everywhere – in my classroom and around the world.

CONTENTS

ALL ABOUT EDDIE

Eddie Woo teaches mathematics at Cherrybrook Technology High School, Sydney. He has been teaching mathematics for more than ten years.

In 2012, Eddie started recording his lessons and uploading them to YouTube – creating 'Wootube'. Since then, he has amassed a following of more than 1 million subscribers and his videos have been viewed more than 60 million times.

In 2018, Eddie was named Australia's Local Hero of the Year and shortlisted as one of the top ten teachers in the world.

A NOTE TO THE READER

This book was made for you to have **FUN** and learn amazing things about the wonders and magic of maths.

Feel free to scribble and make notes all over the pages.

There are plenty of fun activities to do. Look out for the activity symbols throughout:

You'll find all the answers to these activities in a TOP SECRET section at the back of the book.
DO NOT PEEK.

Most importantly, don't forget to
ENJOY MATHS!

ARE YOU READY FOR

YOUR MATHS ADVENTURE?

Excellent. But first, you need to take a
Very Important Quiz:

Do you have:	YES	NO
1 head	☐	☐
1 brain	☐	☐
1 pencil or pen	☐	☐
2 eyes (there's so much maths to see in the world around us)	☐	☐
1 copy of **EDDIE WOO'S MAGICAL MATHS 2**	☐	☐
1 water bottle	☐	☐

★★★★ BONUS QUESTION ★★★★

Add up all the numbers mentioned on these 2 pages.

My answer is: _____

Answers

6 OUT OF 6: Congratulations. A star for you. You have everything you need. You are ready to begin. Good luck!

5 OUT OF 6: So close! Just one more thing to get. I'll wait for you.

4 OUT OF 6: Hmm. You are missing some Very Important Things. You may take a little longer to get yourself together.

3 AND BELOW: Hmm. Hmmmm. You are missing Even More Very Important Things (quite possibly a head, or a brain . . .). This may not be the quiz for you.

Numbers make the world go round.

THE NUM

BER FILES

They are inside and outside you and me and everyone.

NUMBER ME

MY NUMBER PROFILE:

Full name _Eddie Woo_

My birthday is _19 September_.

I have _1_ sister(s).

I have _1_ brother(s).

I have _3_ children.

I have written _3_ books.

I have _0_ pets.

NUMBER YOU

YOUR NUMBER PROFILE:

PASTE YOUR PHOTO HERE

Full name _____

I am _____ years old.

My birthday is _____ .

My best friend is _____ years old.

I have _____ sister(s).

I have _____ brother(s).

I have _____ eyes.

I have _____ legs.

I have _____ arms.

I have _____ heart.

I have _____ kidneys.

I have _____ liver.

There are _____ kids in my class.

My lucky number is _____.

I know ___ times tables off by heart.

I know _____ poems.

I have _____ pets.

I have _____ freckles.

I know _____ jokes.

This is my favourite joke:

_____

_____

_____

NUMBERS IN A NAME

This is my *second* Magical Maths book so I've called it

EDDIE WOO'S MAGICAL MATHS 2

I know! What a great title.

2 X 2 INTERESTING FACTS ABOUT THE NUMBER 2:

FACT NO.1

2 doesn't look like a prime number but it is. It's the smallest prime number.

FACT NO.2

2 is the only prime number that is an **EVEN NUMBER.**

I'm *SPECIAL.*

I'm special **2!**

2, 3, 5, 7, 11, 13, 17, 19

FACT NO.3

2 and **3** are the only **2** consecutive prime numbers.

FACT NO.4

Some people believe **2** is a lucky number because good things can come in pairs.

Psst: Bad things can come in **3**s (although you can be third time lucky **2**!).

You can be all at **6**s and **7**s (how confusing!).

And **2** heads are better than **1** (although possibly crowded if on the **1** body).

A stitch in time can save **9**.

You can be on cloud **9** (if clouds **1–8** are already taken).

A Add up all the numbers on these pages.

My answer is: _____

How to

DRAW A 3D '2'

'DOODLE TWO'

Step 1:

2

Step 2:

Step 3:

Step 4:

Step 5:

Step 6: *VOILA!*

SEARCHING FOR

2

 All the words in this word search are synonyms for two. Can you find them?

twin   double   pair   duo   duet   duplet
binary   dual   both   couple

```
W  E  R  B  T  Y  U  I  O  P  L  K  J  H  G  B
A  D  Q  M  O  N  B  V  C  X  Z  A  S  D  F  I
S  U  D  W  E  T  R  T  T  Y  D  U  B  F  O  N
L  P  U  P  C  Z  H  P  G  N  O  A  P  Q  V  A
Q  L  M  W  N  E  R  B  T  V  U  Y  D  S  U  R
N  E  D  J  T  Z  O  U  D  Q  B  X  K  A  E  Y
H  T  F  U  T  W  I  N  A  K  L  Z  V  N  D  O
P  S  I  Z  Q  L  F  S  C  B  E  R  D  U  A  L
E  L  K  R  N  A  J  A  O  P  F  B  G  Z  Q  J
H  A  L  V  E  K  Z  O  Q  W  R  T  E  T  Y  B
L  K  J  H  G  F  T  D  S  A  Z  X  C  V  N  M
E  D  C  R  F  V  T  G  B  Y  H  N  U  J  K
P  O  I  Y  U  T  J  Q  Z  O  I  A  C  K  A  T
K  E  D  U  O  G  A  S  W  A  L  P  E  O  Z  E
L  S  F  G  J  U  I  X  P  B  N  E  I  L  I  U
C  O  U  P  L  E  P  Q  L  A  S  D  F  G  H  D
```

HAPPY

bee

FLASH FACT:
World Bee Day
is celebrated
on 20 May.

DAY

Honeybees can **ADD** and **SUBTRACT.**

This is **AMAZING** but True.

They may have really tiny bee brains but researchers in the
United States trained some honeybees to
add and subtract by 1.

FLASH FACT:
Bees tell other bees where
there are flowers by doing
a special dance that indicates
the direction and distance
to fly in. We call this a
'vector' in mathematics.

If bees can do it, so can you.
But as your brains are SO MUCH BIGGER than
bee brains, I think you need a **bigger** challenge.

This is a SPEED TEST so are you ready?

READY, SET, GO!

Adding up as *fast* as you can:

7 + 6 = _____

20 + 5 = _____

31 + 6 = _____

8 + 22 = _____

46 + 4 = _____

18 + 15 = _____

32 + 32 = _____

19 + 3 = _____

64 + 5 = _____

124 + 123 = _____

Subtracting as *fast* as you can:

7 - 6 = _____

20 - 5 = _____

31 - 6 = _____

22 - 8 = _____

46 - 4 = _____

18 - 15 = _____

32 – 32 = _____

19 - 3 = _____

64 - 5 = _____

124 - 123 = _____

A Draw your starting and finishing times.

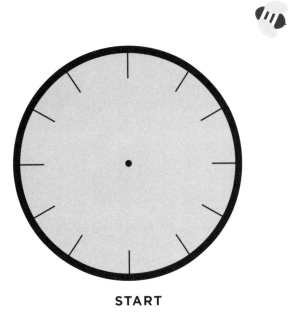

START

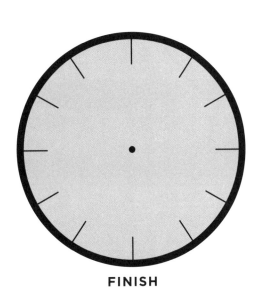

FINISH

RECORD BOX

BEAT YOURSELF
I completed the speed test in _____ minutes.

BEAT YOUR FRIEND
_____ completed the speed test in _____ minutes.

BEAT ME
Eddie completed the speed test in _3_____ minutes.

BRAVO

YOU ARE AS FAST AS A HONEYBEE.

Fill in the missing similes:

As brave as a _____.

As boring as watching _____ dry.

As cunning as a _____.

As cool as a _____.

As dead as a _____.

As fresh as a _____.

As loose as a _____.

As quiet as a _____.

As regular as _____.

As sour as _____.

BEE

BUZZ

16

Count the honeybees buzzing on this page.

NUMBERS IN DISGUISE

Numbers often dress up as fractions, decimals and percentages.

But don't be fooled by the way they look. Fractions, decimals and percentages are just different ways of saying the same number.

For example:
½ = 0.5 = 50%

 Can you complete the rest of this table?

fraction	decimal	percentage
¼		
½		
¾		
⅕		
⅖		
⅗		
⅘		
⅓		
⅔		

THE
WHOLE
WHOLE
STORY

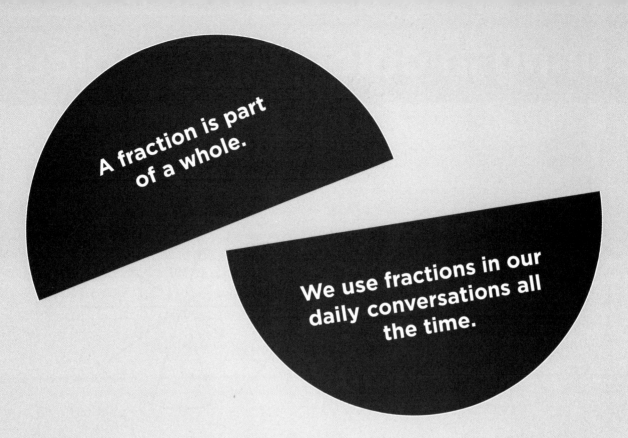

A fraction is part of a whole.

We use fractions in our daily conversations all the time.

Here's an imagined conversation between you and *me*:

I've run **HALF** the marathon.

WOW. Only 21 km to go!

I've read a **THIRD** of my book.

The best part happens halfway through.

It's **QUARTER** past nine.

OH NO. You're 15 minutes late for maths.

 Colour in the fractions written underneath each shape.

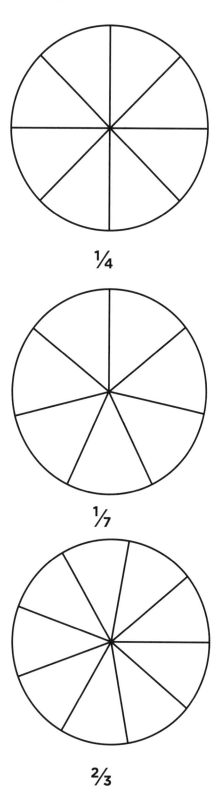

¼

⅐

⅔

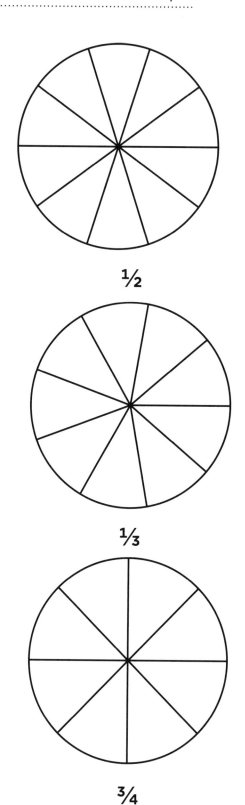

½

⅓

¾

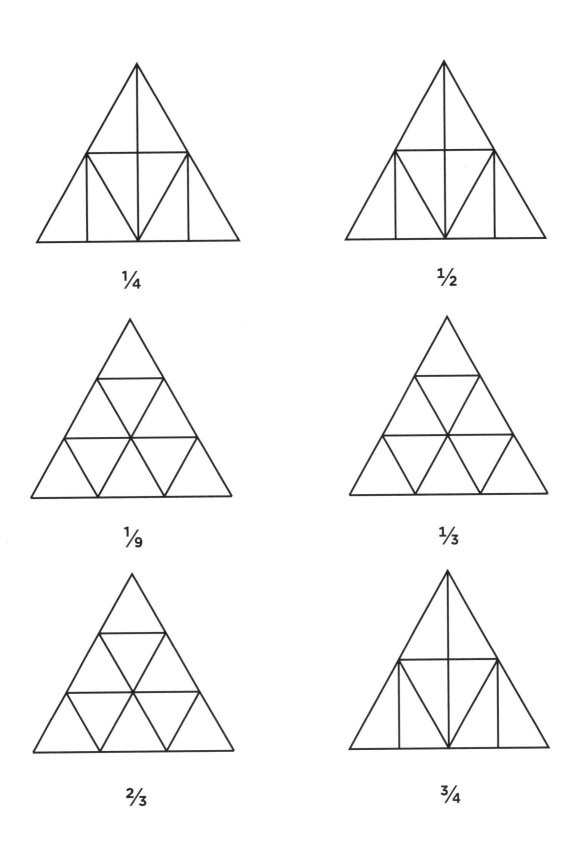

¼

½

⅑

⅓

⅔

¾

A fraction

is made up

of three parts:

the Numerator,

the Denominator

and the

Vinculum.

I think they

all sound like

superheroes.

SUPERHERO
SPOTLIGHT!

THE NUMERATOR:

This is the number above the line and it's the number of equal parts. In proper fractions, it is smaller than the Denominator. In improper fractions, it is larger than the Denominator.

THE VINCULUM:

This is the line separating the two numbers. But a line is never just a line in maths. The Vinculum joins the Numerator and the Denominator. It's like the glue between them.

FLASH FACT: The division sign ÷, also called an obelus, is basically a fraction with the Numerator and Denominator missing!

THE DENOMINATOR:

This is the number below the line and it says how many of the Numerator's equal parts make up a whole.

There's fraction friction between the Numerator
and the Denominator.

NUMERATOR VS

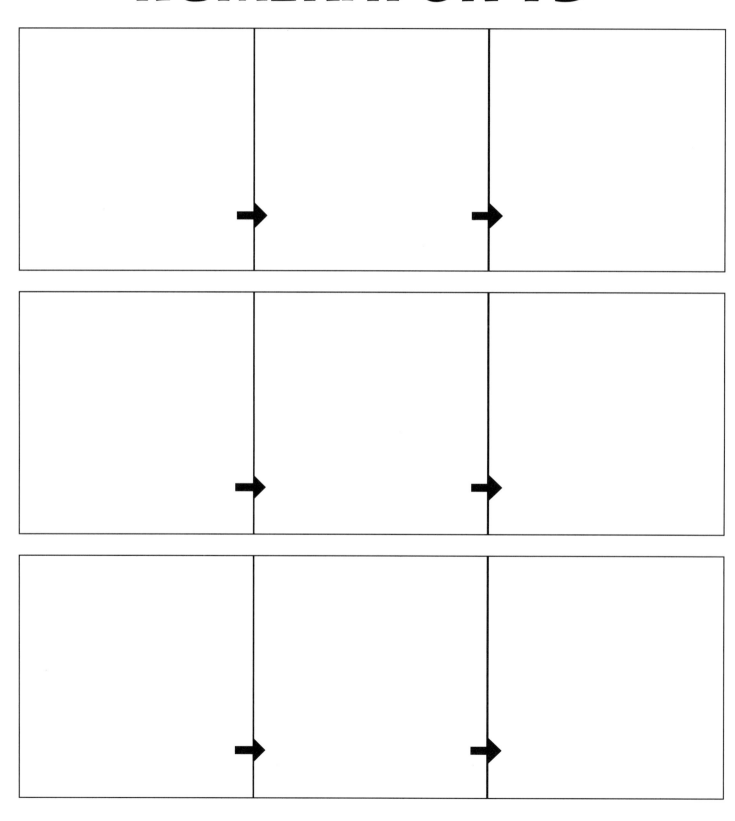

Create a storyboard – using pictures and words – plotting out the action. Make your story as dramatic as you can.

DENOMINATOR

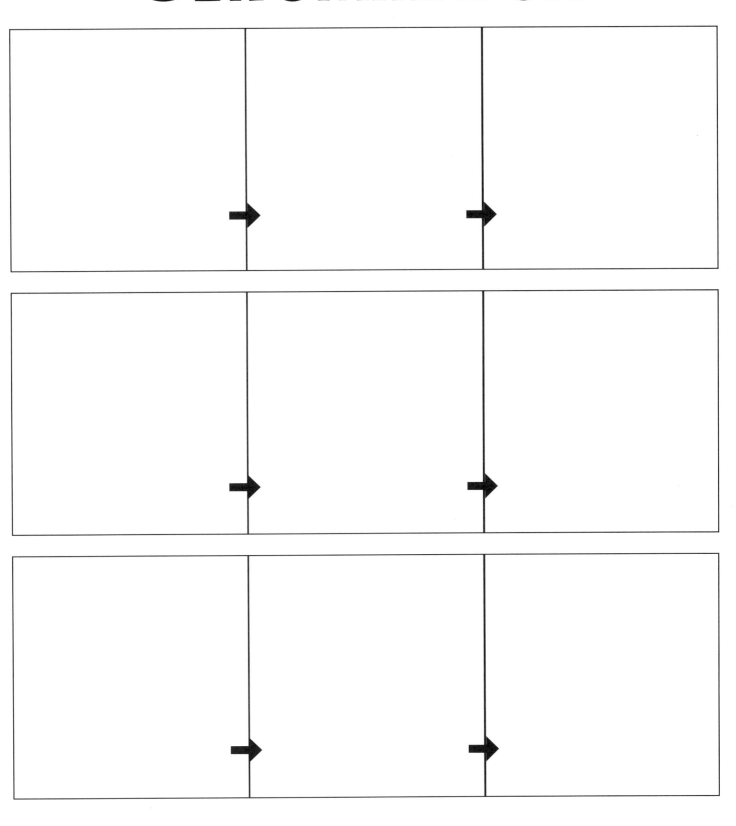

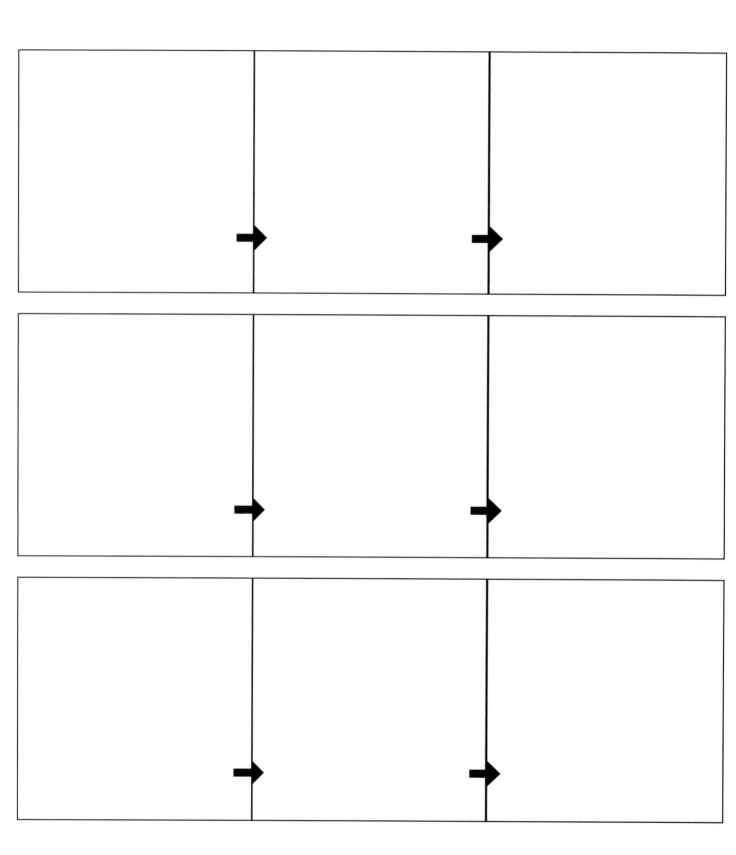

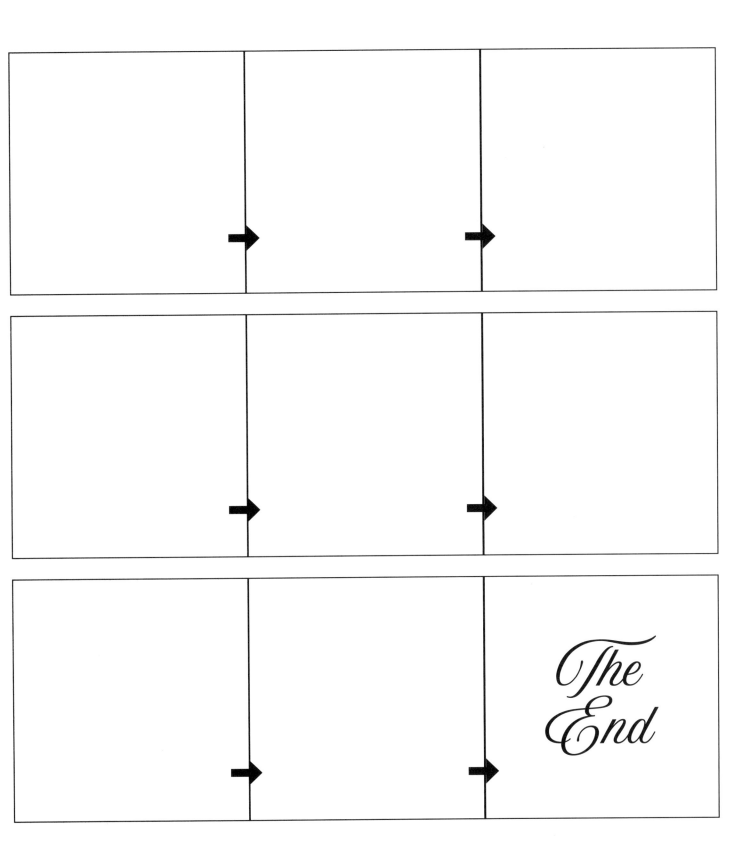

The End

A PIE IN THE SKY

What are your Top Three favourite kinds of pies?

1. ______________________________

2. ______________________________

3. ______________________________

NB: Dividing pies evenly is a very important life skill and you should learn how to do this as soon as possible.

If you ever have to divide a pie between your friends or your family, you'll be very pleased you know all about fractions. They are the best way to split pies evenly.

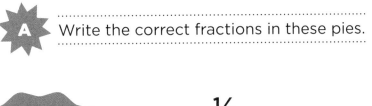

A Write the correct fractions in these pies.

1⁄3
3⁄4
3⁄5
2⁄3
1⁄2
2⁄5
1⁄5
4⁄5
1⁄4

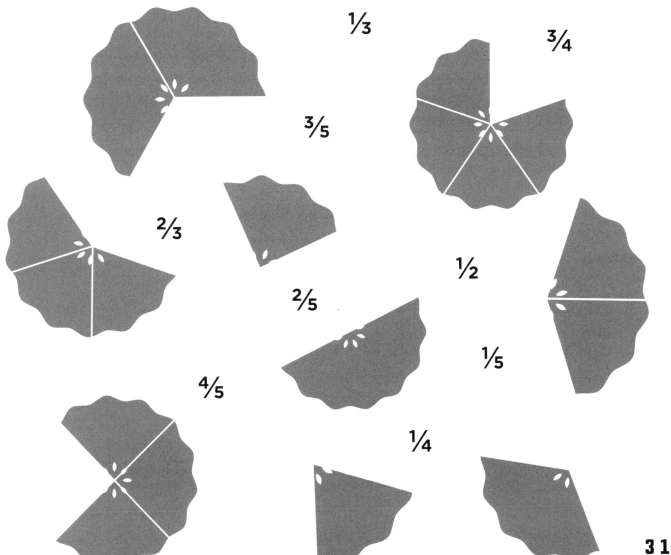

MAKING A POINT

Decimals are based on multiples of 10 and a decimal is very precise.

It represents a whole number plus a fraction of a whole number (such as tenths, hundredths . . .).

When we go shopping, the price of the things we buy is written in decimals, for example: $19.25.

The decimal point is the most important part of a decimal number. Without it, we would be at 6s and 7s, trying to work out what the number was.

$19.25

WE INTERRUPT THIS PAGE WITH A

WARNING

YOU NEED TO KNOW YOUR **LEFTS** AND **RIGHTS** FOR THE NEXT PART SO TIME TO DO A QUICK REFRESHER QUIZ:

*Psst: If you can use both hands equally well for some or all of these tasks, you are very clever. You can call yourself **ambidextrous.***

I write with my _____ hand.

I wave with my _____ hand.

I eat with my _____ hand.

I play a ukulele with my _____ hand.

A Can you identify all the parts of a decimal?

The number to the ⬅ of the point is the whole number.

So, in $19.25, the whole number is _____.

The **first** number to the ➡ of the point is in the 'tenths' position.

So, in $19.25, the number in the tenths spot is _____.

The **second** number to the ➡ of the point is in the 'hundredths' spot.

So, in $19.25, the number in the hundredths spot is _____.

% PERCENTAGES %

If you want to compare two different quantities, percentages are the things for you.

The word 'per cent' is a Latin word that means 'out of a hundred' and the symbol for percent is %.

The grids on the opposite page all contain 100 little squares.

FLASH FACT:
100 years is a century.
A 100th anniversary
is a centenary.

Colour in the following percentages on the grids:

Psst: The first one is done for you.

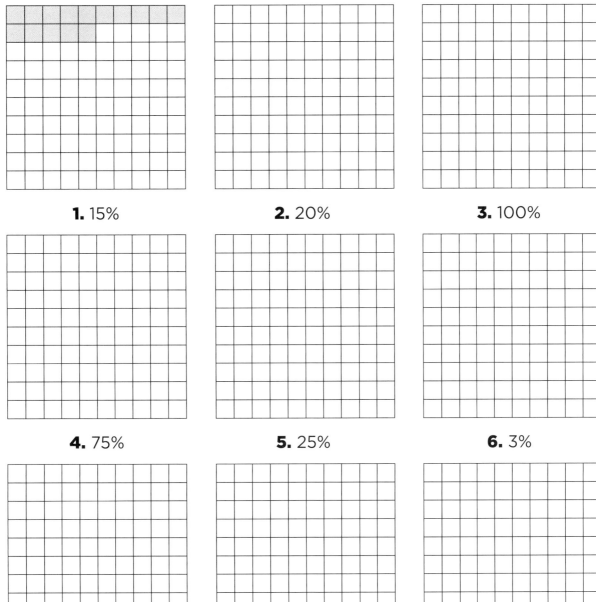

1. 15%   **2.** 20%   **3.** 100%

4. 75%   **5.** 25%   **6.** 3%

7. 30%   **8.** 99%   **9.** 6%

 Now look at the uncoloured parts of each grid. What percentages are they?

1.   6.

2.   7.

3.   8.

4.   9.

5.

3 5

Time is commonly measured in fractions.

Psst: There are digital, 12-hour and 24-hour clocks.

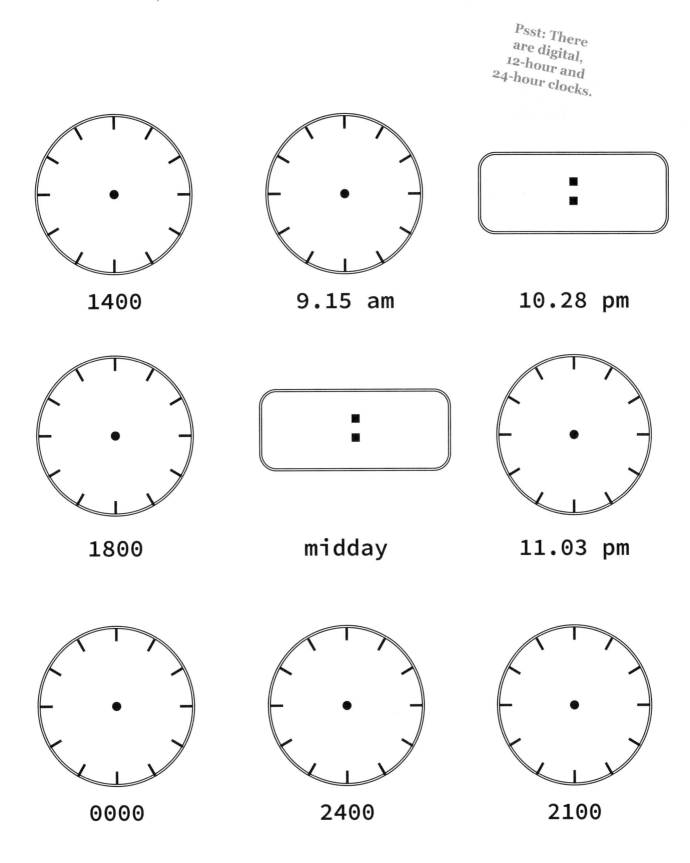

1400

9.15 am

10.28 pm

1800

midday

11.03 pm

0000

2400

2100

3 7

MAKE YOUR OWN CLOCK

You will need

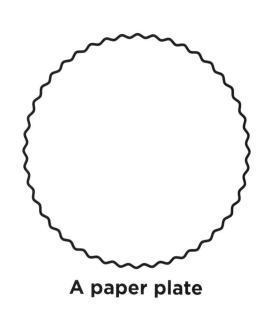

A paper plate

A brad pin

A pair of scissors

A ruler

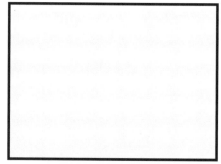

A sheet of coloured cardboard

A marker

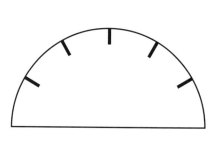

A protractor

1. Using your ruler, mark lightly the 12, 3, 6 and 9 spots. Also make a small mark in the middle of the plate:

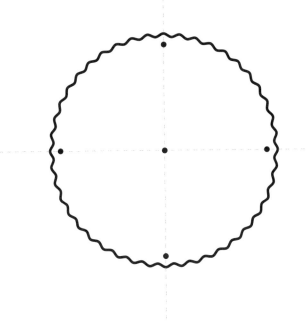

2. Using your protractor, mark up the 1, 2, 4, 5, 7, 8, 10 and 11 spots. They are at 30° from the previous number:

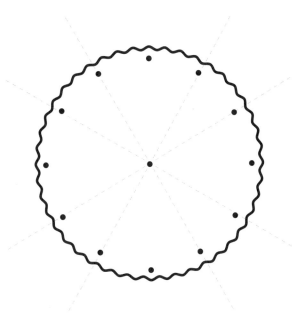

3. Using your marker, draw all your numbers onto your clock:

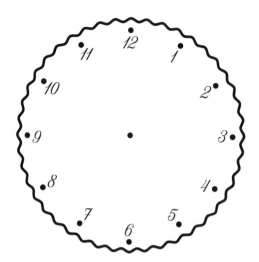

4. Using your scissors, cut two arrows from your coloured card board. Make one slightly longer than the other. With your marker, make dots at the bottom of each arrow:

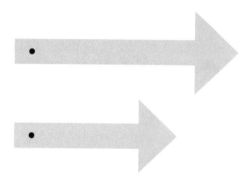

5. Place both arrows on top of the paper plate, lining up the dots on the arrows with the dot in the centre of the plate:

6. Push the brad pin through the dots of the arrows and clock, securing them together. Fasten the brad pin:

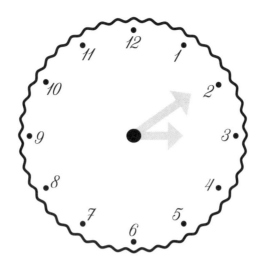

7. Voila! Your very own clock! The longer arrow is the minute arrow, and the shorter arrow is the hour arrow:

PRIME

TIME

I  PRIME NUMBERS

 A Join the dots so Prime can arrive with PANACHE!

37 •

29 •

31 •

5 •

3 •

7 •

2 •

23

11 • 97 •

19 •

13 •

17 •

They are ROCKSTARS in the world of maths.

41

43

79

47

83

73

53

89

59

71

61

67

A   Now, colour me!

I know **YOU** know that ***PRIME NUMBERS*** have 2 factors. They are <u>whole numbers</u> that can <u>only be divided evenly by themselves and 1.</u>

BUT

did you know that prime numbers are

so much more?

In fact, they are the

! MOST IMPORTANT NUMBERS IN MATHS !

FAMOUS MATHS MAN

A Greek mathematician called **Euclid** was the first **1** to realise this. He discovered that every single number greater than **1** is either a prime or can be 'built' by multiplying prime numbers.

I'm in my prime.

Look at these numbers up to 10 to see what Euclid means:

2 = prime

3 = prime

4 = 2 x 2

5 = prime

6 = 3 x 2

7 = prime

8 = 2 x 2 x 2

9 = 3 x 3

10 = 5 x 2

This fact about prime numbers is so mathematically important it gets a fancy name and a page to itself:

The

FUNDAMENTAL

THEOREM *of*

ARITHMETIC

PRIME NUMBERS ARE THE ELEMENTS

3   5   17   19   37   41   59   61   79   83

OF THE MATHEMATICAL UNIVERSE

Only,

lonely

<u>one</u>

Prime numbers

have *2 factors*

but the

number 1

has only

one.

If **1** were a prime number,
the *Fundamental Theorem of Arithmetic* **wouldn't**
work because there would be
several ways to write each number –
not just one.

FUN WITH THE

We didn't want **1** to feel left out so three of them have gate-crashed this party of prime numbers.
Can you spot them?

54

NUMBER ONE

55

Colour in only the PRIME NUMBERS to reveal the animal hiding in the grid.

4	52	27	33	75	36	55	14	82	9	81	87	12	10	28	4	21	44	75	62
84	65	32	44	6	50	63	42	91	46	63	90	74	56	22	77	16	52	84	91
20	51	76	18	92	35	4	28	70	15	52	45	18	6	14	30	20	69	72	48
12	91	9	46												8	49	56	74	86	85
85	72	36	54												51	34	15	58	70	81
63	14	81	6	30	56	10	65	82	9	16	27	25	38	63	65	9	24	36	55
32	52	2	21	87	4	21	6	80	15	22	52	4	62	56	32	75	92	40	98
45	81	90	46	99	28	76	24	35	50	45	60	12	8	91	66	84	8	54	95
12	26	15	8	14	33	40	10	42	57	68	76	25	21	80	45	39	76	82	56
22	4	10	63	27	18	34	54	26	63	74	90	6	46	88	93	85	55	4	75
9	25	56	74	9	20	49	70	56	90	87	85	91	10	94	26	42	68	99	57
27	80	21	32	16	91	25	82	8	75	86	10	18	27	62	72	90	9	63	70
6	14	55	44	28	45	72	38	64	15	36	9	49	22	58	92	69	44	73	29
52	62	87	50	12	55	69	90	77	27	96	93	76	33	75	64	71	5	3	61
20	76	35	66	72	24	84	51	93	68	87	45	98	82	50	67	23	11	17	67
40	58	7	30	80	65	46	76	74	91	4	84	77	13	79	53	47	13	73	31
64	16	29	61	42	33	81	92	8	88	85	48	2	43	11	29	19	5	71	5
75	51	39	13	5	73	70	87	38	66	57	52	29	61	53	31	67	43	97	23
26	85	95	53	23	83	17	45	63	34	5	79	11	53	67	17	79	59	61	13
92	60	24	56	41	47	59	31	67	97	71	47	3	31	13	23	41	17	3	53
48	81	65	72	54	3	11	43	2	11	83	53	67	23	59	97	5	31	67	29
12	52	57	46	63	42	58	37	19	61	19	31	17	71	43	83	7	11	19	97
27	68	30	82	78	6	21	50	4	13	23	59	29	67	11	2	47	73	83	5
8	45	70	87	60	92	45	88	65	24	51	38	53	73	7	97	53	89	23	67
51	66	84	91	55	16	33	76	80	12	77	10	67	17	43	19	13	59	17	29
34	22	81	75	48	26	57	54	22	68	62	49	14	59	3	41	23	61	47	13
15	62	56	86	39	64	93	16	40	35	24	27	6	83	79	89	7	2	16	52
54	36	72	10	87	9	86	28	9	56	84	69	58	5	47	29	11	97	40	74
50	69	4	78	80	77	44	12	6	70	92	75	30	86	65	55	82	78	56	4
25	58	65	32	46	52	90	74	82	21	63	18	42	91	48	60	76	81	25	33

56	68	88	6	45	38	50	26	70	62	85	54	9	80	93	57	65	22	49	35
82	50	63	4	33	14	28	82	66	42	36	69	39	25	76	10	91	78	6	58
58	34	70	80	54	64	46	33	74	51	2	7	97	60	27	85	34	55	40	20
77	92	46	65	26	49	24	57	21	3	89	71	37	23	30	45	68	52	32	75
55	69	52	91	39	6	68	81	44	11	5	89	13	19	47	53	16	76	84	99
62	36	90	8	86	35	75	25	9	59	43	3	97	73	41	61	23	46	72	88
72	48	66	4	30	63	56	80	48	10	61	2	17	43	13	5	29	38	91	14
81	57	78	16	58	16	58	36	52	68	23	67	79	66	51	8	96	9	82	56
65	4	85	74	21	46	72	22	76	4	37	97	31	76	28	12	62	69	12	33
50	75	22	87	35	42	69	45	55	30	41	17	5	32	70	54	24	87	44	90
64	46	60	12	68	8	24	60	78	12	53	11	71	15	36	4	22	65	92	8
27	63	82	42	76	20	32	54	26	66	19	83	47	9	63	48	74	16	35	10
5	2	28	93	55	38	51	70	62	13	2	59	82	56	82	99	86	26	95	78
31	37	83	6	24	27	65	18	64	3	97	61	25	90	49	24	15	93	18	64
83	5	17	37	41	44	34	74	6	19	43	5	72	69	91	98	75	62	55	30
67	89	19	71	19	7	48	40	79	31	61	37	46	94	27	76	36	4	18	74
43	73	47	3	43	5	9	32	53	11	89	41	82	50	16	39	14	72	33	6
31	19	2	11	67	2	59	41	83	29	17	7	32	75	6	10	52	99	51	66
5	59	89	97	17	89	29	3	97	73	41	61	8	99	51	74	20	40	70	88
83	2	23	19	3	53	7	19	61	2	13	83	26	42	76	16	28	32	21	9
37	53	79	83	29	67	41	29	17	67	11	60	93	34	84	9	81	46	65	15
97	61	5	7	19	11	13	83	73	59	43	18	64	90	78	62	10	75	92	21
47	83	11	2	67	53	2	23	5	13	49	28	80	98	44	95	72	68	26	86
2	89	17	59	19	37	41	61	7	20	58	63	92	22	87	21	14	94	12	74
37	53	29	3	41	89	17	59	21	35	72	46	85	66	14	6	25	42	80	96
19	5	97	13	31	43	9	52	74	57	78	88	91	38	57	98	64	85	99	51
32	47	83	29	53	11	24	39	15	4	75	30	24	96	69	40	6	10	84	36
21	13	2	37	79	5	28	70	62	81	55	76	95	74	78	92	48	27	93	46
77	54	10	63	44	12	32	51	45	68	84	33	86	60	22	54	90	35	58	70
14	38	57	72	18	26	48	36	10	56	65	42	8	16	82	63	75	50	4	39

Prime rhyme

Write a poem about your favourite prime number by following these 3 easy steps.

1. Think of a prime number.

2. Think of all the things that rhyme with that number, for example, if 3 is your favourite prime (excellent choice!) you might think of:

bee →   see page 10

flea →   can leap amazingly high

free

knee →   we have two of these

me →   that's you

sea

see

pea →   my favourite vegetables

plea →   more maths, please

tree →   this is a fractal, see page 72

we →   you, me and everyone

3. Write your poem.

MY PRIME-RHYME POEM

Written by: _____

_____

_____

_____

_____

_____

_____

_____

_____

_____

_____

_____

_____

_____

_____

_____

_____

The End

It was late at night in the Prime Lab.
3, **5**, and **7** were working on the *Euclid–Mullin sequence* when
they noticed a number of strange things:

1. It was dark.

2. They had forgotten to eat dinner.

3. There was a number missing.

'There's a number missing,' said **3**.

'You're right,' said **7**.

'It can't be far away,' said **5**, checking his pocket.
'Numbers can't run.'

'But they can hide,' said **7**. 'Numbers are hidden all around us.
The universe is so infinite.'

'This is no time to be deep, **7**,' said **3**, with a sigh. 'And we don't have to
search the universe. Just this lab.'

'If we don't find that missing number, we can't finish
our sequence,' said **5**.

'Spread out,' said **3**.

★ ★ ★ ★ **BONUS QUESTION** ★ ★ ★ ★

Add up all the numbers mentioned on this page.

Psst: Don't forget to double check. Even triple check. (A quadruple check might be **1** check too many.)

My answer is: _____

SUSPECT LINE-UP

43   13   53

1. There are _____ wonders of the Ancient World.

2. There are _____ blind mice.

Add these two numbers together.

Your answer: _____

3. There are _____ years in a century.

Multiply your answer from 1 and 2 by this number.

Your answer: _____

A

One of these numbers in the line-up is the missing one.
Fill in the blanks in the footprints and work out
the maths to discover which number it is.

5

62271

3878320571

Multiply your answer to Footprint 5 by two.

Your answer: _____

5. There are _____ letters in the alphabet.

Add your answer to Footprint 4.

4. There are _____ Arabian Nights.

THE PRIME SUSPECT IS:

Subtract your answer to Footprint 4 from your final answer to Footprint 3.

Your answer: _____

_____

MATHS ABOUT!

Maths is here,

maths is there,

maths is . . .

EVERY WHERE.

This is because the world around us

is filled with all kinds of amazing,

never-ending patterns – from the florets of a flower

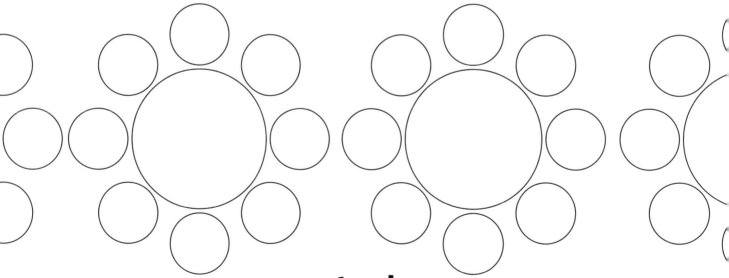

to the thousands of raindrops in a rainbow.

 Colour in these flowers to make them bloom across the page.

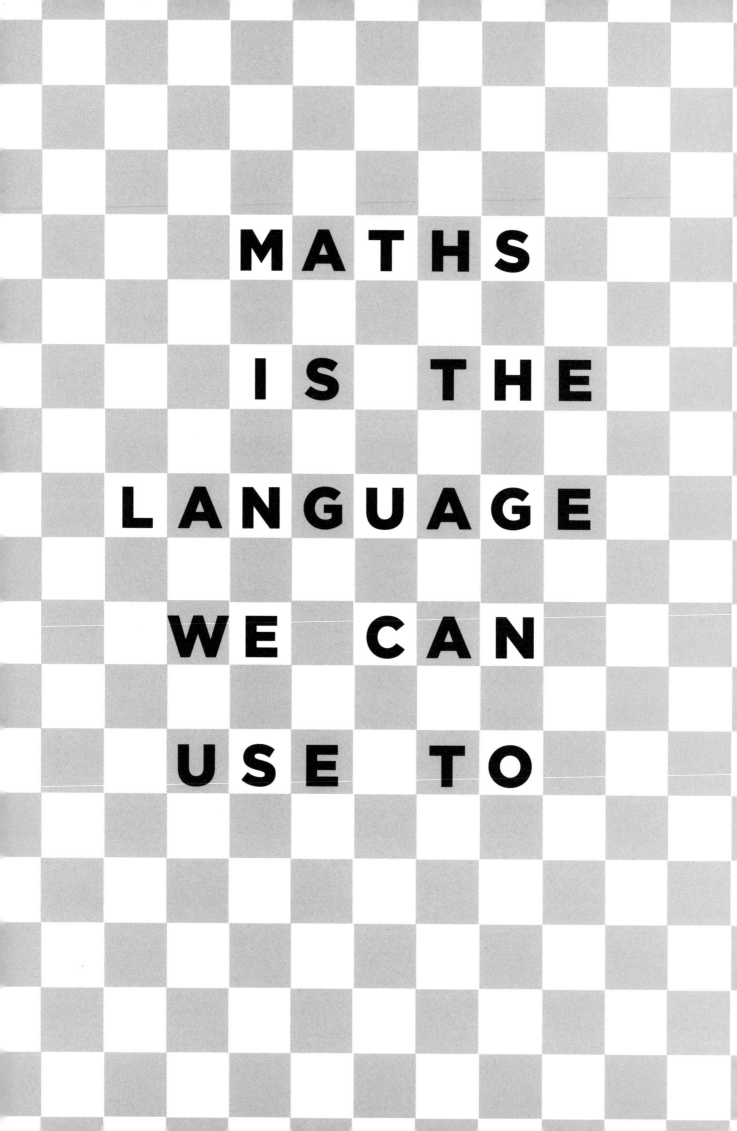

MATHS

IS THE

LANGUAGE

WE CAN

USE TO

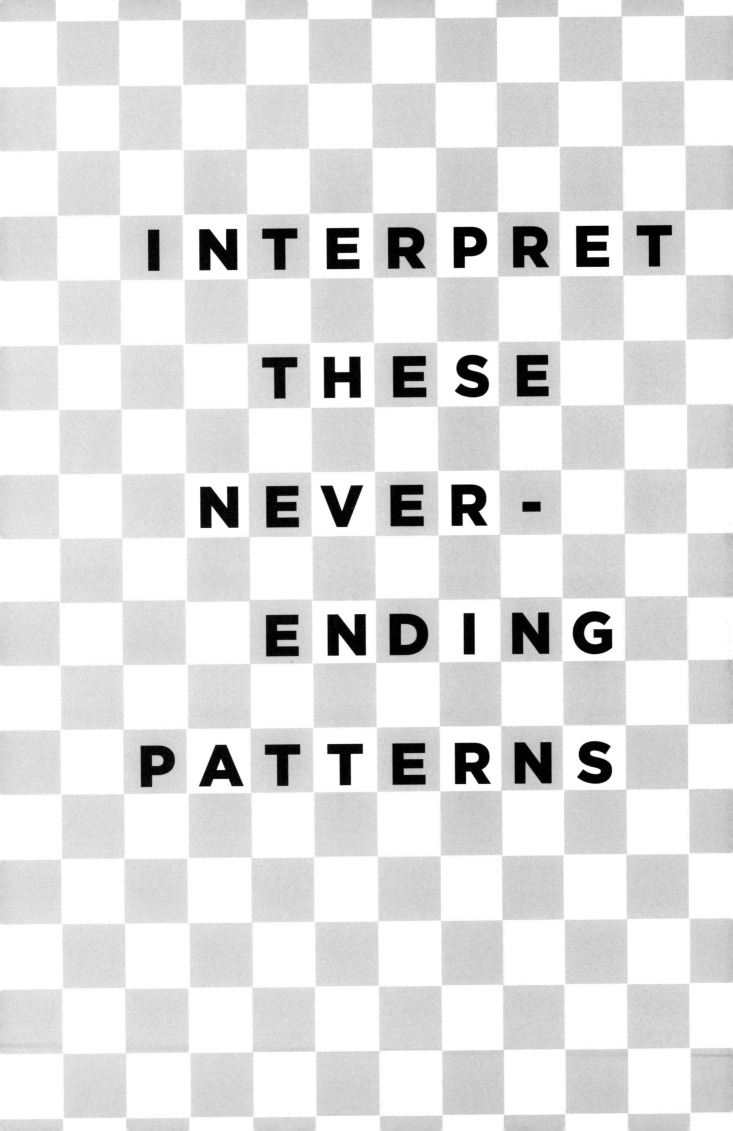

INTERPRET THESE NEVER-ENDING PATTERNS

FINDING OUT ABOUT FRACTALS

These never-ending patterns are called fractals.

Fractals are repeating patterns that get smaller and smaller as they repeat.

A Continue this pattern for the rest of this page.

Nature is **FULL** of fractals.

A galaxy is one of the

BIGGEST

LOST IN SPACE

A

Help the spaceship find its way to the centre of this spiral galaxy.

Psst: Get ready to duck, dive and DODGE asteroids as you zip through space.

ENTER HERE

THE

SHAPE

OF

SNOW

A snowflake is one of the smallest fractals.

Every single snowflake is different.

 Can you spot the 19 differences between these two snowflakes?

Fractals can
branch

A Can you name all these branching fractals?

_____

_____

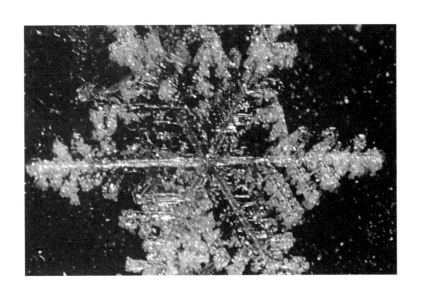

Fractals can
spiral

A Can you name all these spiralling fractals?

_____

THE FATHER OF FRACTALS

A mathematician called Benoit Mandelbrot was the first person to study and name fractals.

He discovered that fractals don't follow straight lines and that some fractal shapes in nature are in fact jagged. Like coastlines.

FLASH FACT:
The word 'fractal' comes from the Latin word 'fractus', which means interrupted, irregular.

Coastline from the Mergui Archipelago in Myanmar

COMPUTER FRACTALS

Mandelbrot was also one of the first people to make fractal images on a computer.

A famous fractal pattern called the

MANDELBROT SET

is named after him.

→

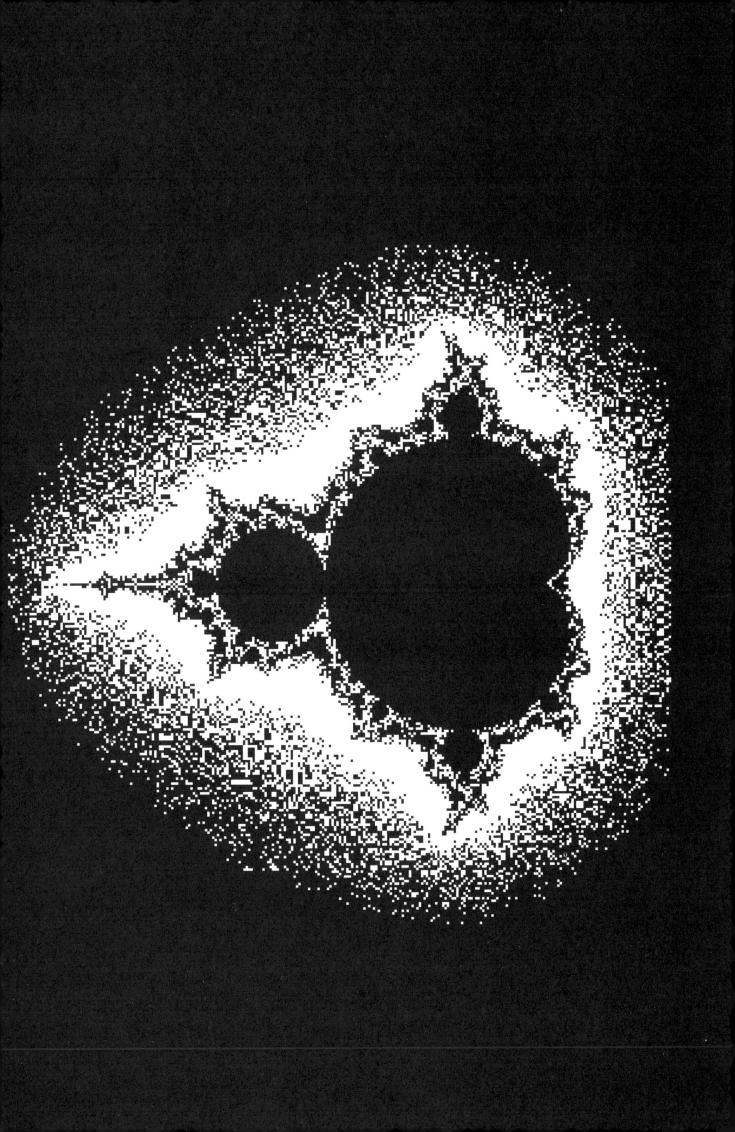

FAMOUS ME

What would you like to be famous for inventing, or creating?

**Maybe a new kind of *FOOD?*
A COMPUTER GAME?**

A TURBO-CHARGED SCOOTER?

Describe your invention:

_____

_____

_____

Draw your invention:

What would you call your invention?

Psst: Make it snappy!

Create an ad for your invention.

Make it as *EYE-CATCHING* as possible. Maybe include some endorsements from your family and friends.

SIERPINSKI FRACTALS

Mathematicians have even created their own fractals.

Wacław Sierpiński, a famous Polish mathematician, developed the **Sierpinski Triangle**.

How to

DRAW A SIERPINSKI TRIANGLE

1. Draw a big triangle. An equilateral one would be good:

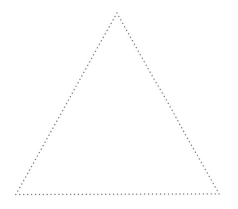

9 3

2. Work out the midpoints of each side of the triangle and mark it:

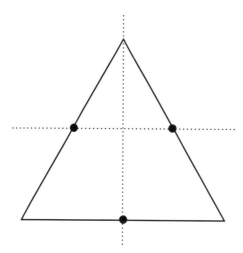

3. Connect these points to form a smaller triangle inside your big triangle:

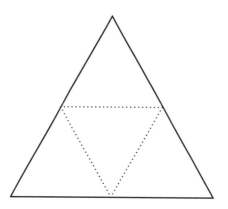

4. Colour in this triangle:

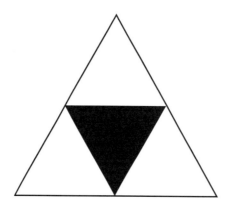

5. Now look at the three uncoloured triangles in the big triangle. Find their midpoints and connect them to make three smaller triangles:

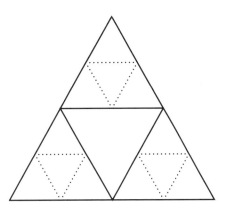

6. Keep going and going and going . . .

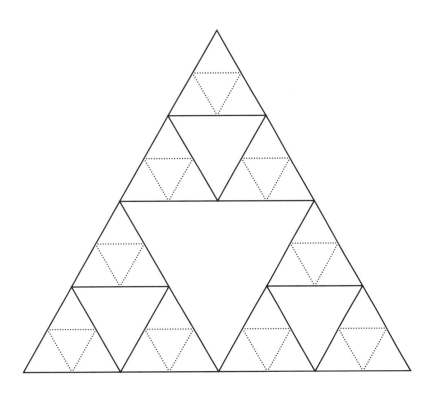

CONGRATULATIONS!

You are the proud maker of
a **Sierpinski Triangle.**

(a very big Sierpinski Triangle)

 Colour in all the triangles within the triangle.

Maths helps us understand the mysteries

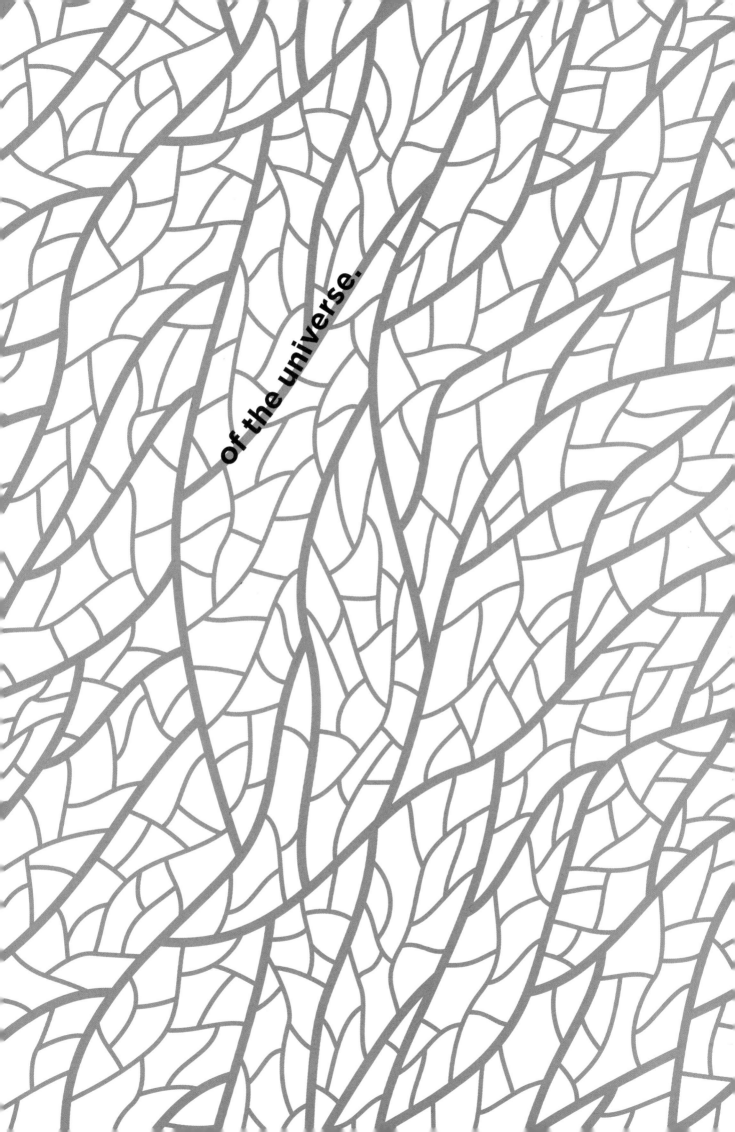

of the universe.

WE ARE MADE OF MATHS

Fractals are also inside us.

If you look at a picture of your lungs, you can see they have the same branching pattern as trees.

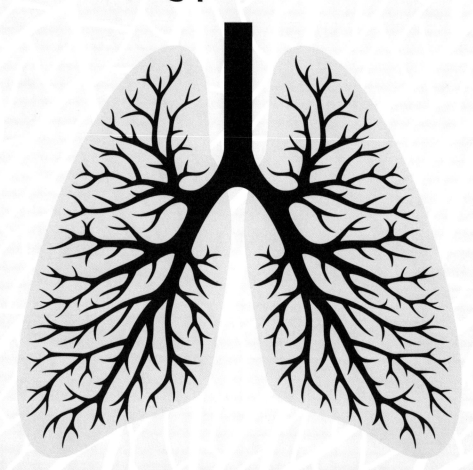

LOOKING AT THE LUNG

Here are *FIVE* fascinating facts about our lungs:

1. They take oxygen from the air and into the bloodstream through all the branching fractals.

2. They remove carbon dioxide from our body.

3. We take up to **20,000** breaths a day.

4. The right lung is bigger than the left lung (that's because the left lung is sharing space with the heart. Another **Very Important** Organ).

5. You can live with only one lung.

>>>Bonus question<<<

If we take **20,000** breaths a day, how many breaths would we take in:

a) a week _____?

b) a 30-day month _____?

c) a year _____?

BRAIN IN A FRAME

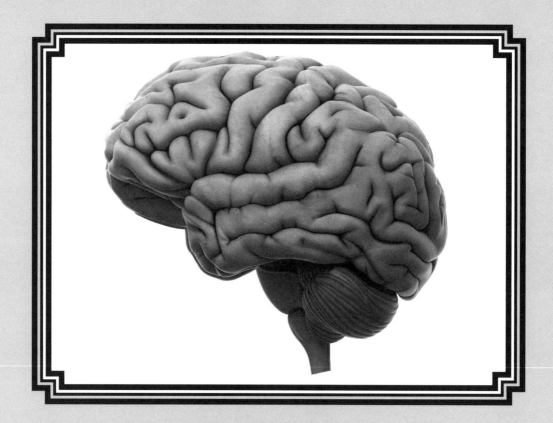

Our brains are the **ULTIMATE** communication machines.

We have **billions and billions** of neurons in our brains and these have **trillions** of connections called synapses.

Our brains are full of branching fractals so that the synapses can communicate with all the cells in our body.

INGENIOUS!

A How many words can you make out of the word *INGENIOUS?*

Psst: There are 122 but DON'T PANIC. You don't need to find all of them.

Can you find 10 words?

MY 10 INGENIOUS WORDS

Here's one to get you started:

1. genius

2. _____

3. _____

4. _____

5. _____

6. _____

7. _____

8. _____

9. _____

10. _____

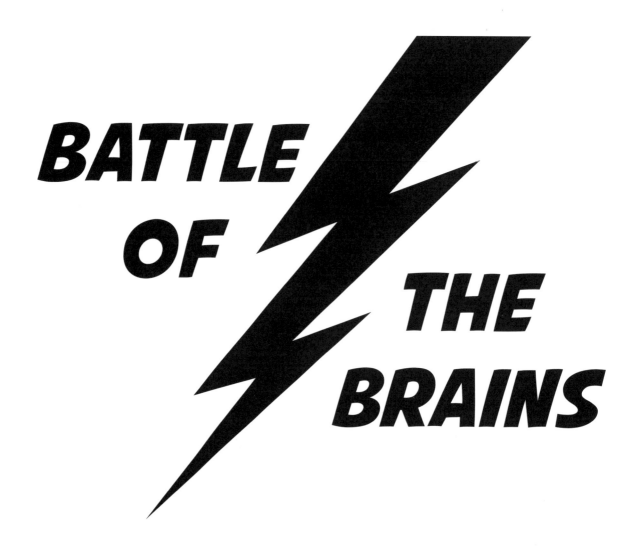

BATTLE OF THE BRAINS

Most animals have a brain.

But there's something soft and spongy that doesn't.

Can you guess what this is?

Your answer: _____

ANIMAL BRAINS

 **A** Can you match these animals with their approximate brain size?

sperm whale	5 kg
elephant	1.7 kg
human	8 kg
killer whale	6 kg
dolphin	1.5 kg
blue whale	6 kg
Triceratops	0.097 kg
goldfish	7 kg

>>>Bonus question<<<

WHO AM I?

I have **32** brains. Show-off.
I rhyme with beach.
I am used in microsurgery.

I am a _____.

BIG

BRAIN

A-MAZE

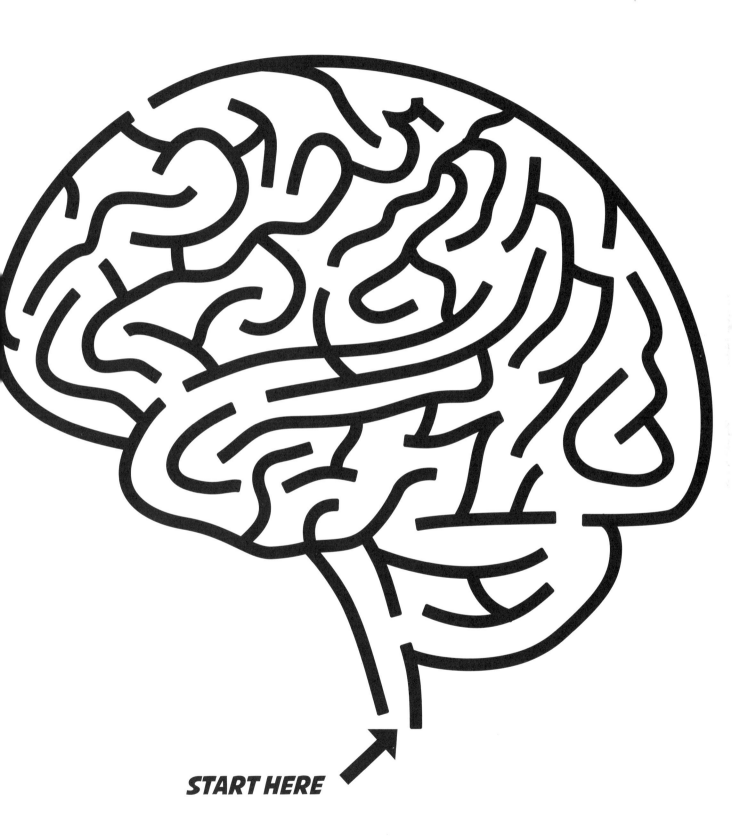

START HERE

MAKE YOUR OWN MOSAIC

You will need

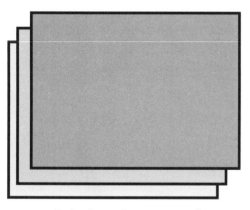

multiple sheets of coloured paper

a sheet of white cardboard

a pencil

a pair of scissors

craft glue

1. On a sheet of white cardboard, draw some shapes.

2. Take your coloured sheets of paper, and cut them up into tiny shapes. Pick a different shape for each colour.

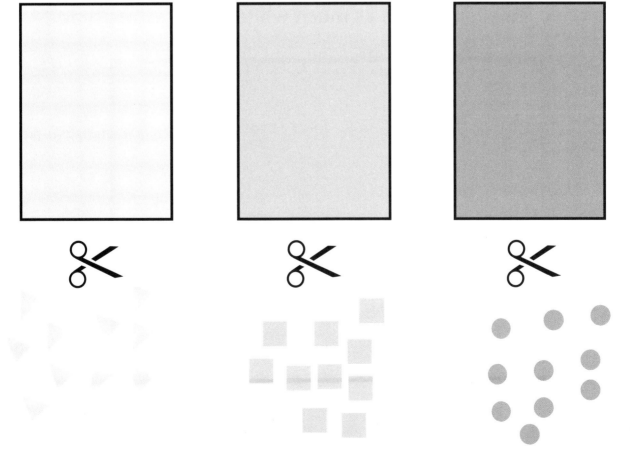

3. Allocate one paper colour to each type of shape drawn on the cardboard. The paper colour shapes CANNOT be the same as the cardboard drawing shape.

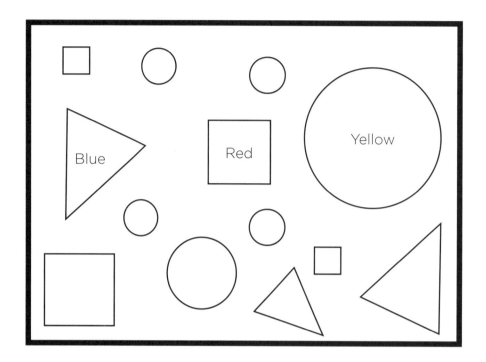

4. Using the glue, start gluing the coloured paper to the assigned shape, covering as much white space as possible.

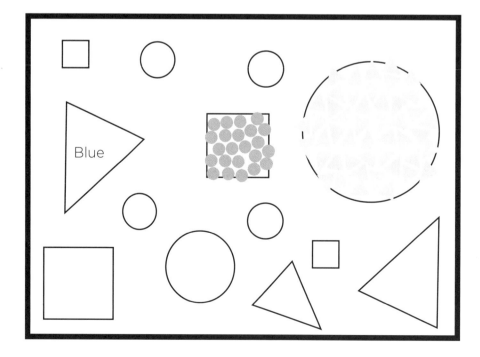

5. Once you have covered all of the shapes, you've made your very first paper-maths-mosaic!

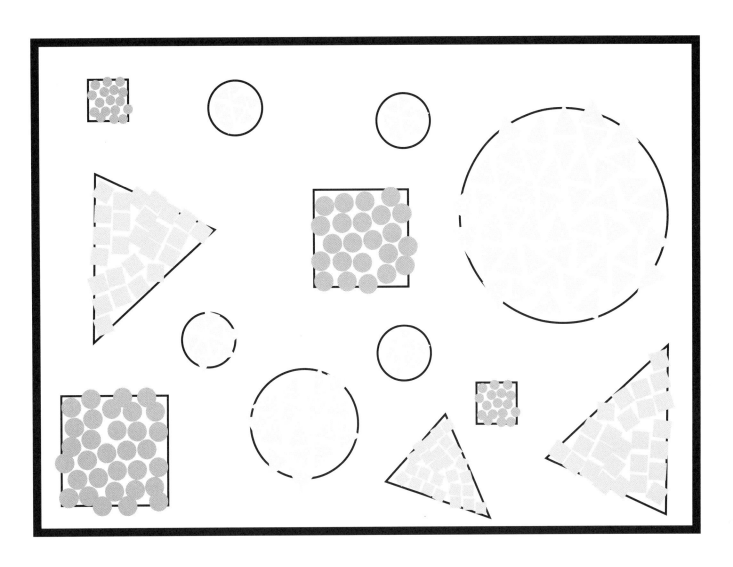

6. You can choose any kind of shape to mosaic. Turn the page for some ideas that you can trace for your next mosaic.

TRACE ME

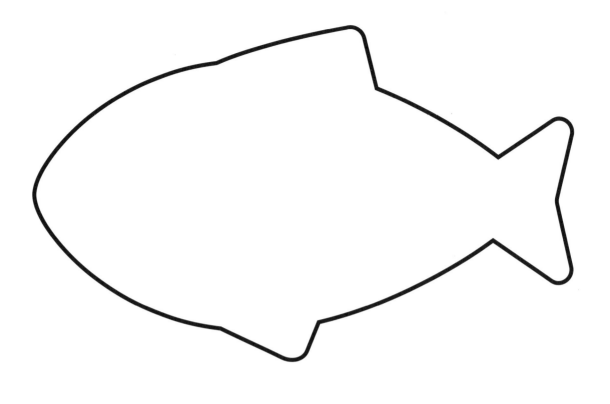

TRACE ME

Keeping secrets is really important, and maths is a secret-keeper's secret weapon to guard his or her words and ideas!

SECRET is a quiet word.

Like *SSSSH*, or *SOFT*, or *SILENCE*, or the sound of *SNOW FALLING*.

A Can you think of some more quiet words?

Psst: Have you noticed how many quiet words start with 's'?

_____

_____

_____

_____

_____

angry

balloons

serene

soft

marshmallow

razzle-dazzle

hushed

doughnut

still

swim

voiceless

noisy

ice cream

deafening

wild

gentle

scream

loud

howling

broccoli

roaring

sombre

yellow

polka dot

low

screaming

clouds

boisterous

zoo

sleep

pizza

shampoo

speechless

agitated

shrill

spaghetti

clamorous

TELLING A SECRET

Sometimes, people whisper secrets to each other.

A Play Telephone with your friends, or family.

1. Sit in a circle.

2. Think of a phrase (make it a good one!) and whisper it to the person on your right.

3. Ask that person to whisper it to the person sitting on his or her right.

4. Continue whispering around and around until the circle is complete.

We started with the phrase:

_____

We ended with the phrase:

_____

OK, so I'm guessing your message tumbled from whisper to whisper until it became a complete jumble.

Am I right?   **YES**   **NO**

There are **THOUSANDS** of maths ways to make sure that messages arrive intact when they are being sent via a computer.

One of these is called the 'check digit'.

Imagine you wanted to send an 8-digit number, for example:

26101949

across to the other side of the world.

Your computer attaches a 9th digit – called a 'check digit' – to the end of your number.

Here's how your computer works out what digit to add to the end of your number:

---

1. It adds up all the digits in the message:
   2 + 6 + 1 + 0 + 1 + 9 + 4 + 9 = 32.
2. It takes this total and then subtracts 10 until the number is less than 10:
   32 – 10 = 22, 22 – 10 = 12, 12 – 10 = 2.
3. The final number (in this case, 2) is the check digit.

When the computer on the other side of the world receives this 9-digit number, it goes through the same steps as your computer (because you have already agreed upon a set of rules for how to do things before you started communicating).

If it gets the same 'check digit' as you, it knows the message has arrived safely.

CHECK!

Sometimes, people write each other messages using invisible ink.

How to

MAKE INVISIBLE INK

You will need

a lemon

a lemon squeezer

water

a cup

a cotton bud

a white piece of paper

1. Squeeze some lemon juice into the cup and add a few drops of water:

2. Mix the water and lemon juice together:

3. Dip the cotton bud into the water and lemon juice:

4. Think about your spectacularly secretive message that you don't want anyone else in the world knowing (apart from the person who is going to get the message):

5. Write your spectacularly secretive message on the paper. When the juice dries, your message will become invisible:

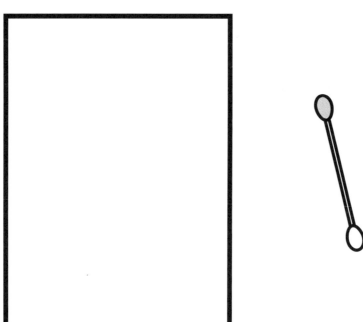

6. To read the message, hold the paper up to a light bulb:

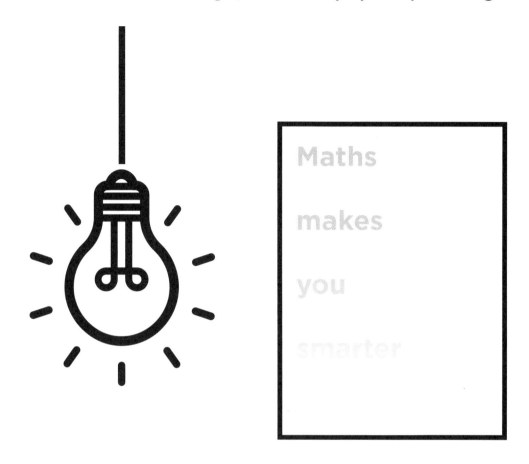

Maths

makes

you

smarter

Write your invisible-ink message here:

_____

_____

_____

_____

People have been sending each other

SECRET MESSAGES

for hundreds of years.

But in the *Old Days*, messengers had to make **long** perilous journeys by land or sea to deliver their messages.

It wasn't a great way to get a **QUICK** response to a message, and the messengers were often captured by their enemies.

These messages were often really easy to intercept.

This lead to the rise of what we now call **ENCRYPTION** – the use of a code to scramble-up messages so that they appear to make no sense at all to anyone who doesn't know how to decipher them.

Looking for a job later in life? You could be a:

Cryptographer   Keeps messages secret.

Cryptanalyst   Cracks the messages.

MIRROR ON THE WALL

A **CRYPTOGRAPHER** and a **CRYPTANALYST** are kind of like mirror images of each other.

A You can also use mirrors to decode secret messages.

1. Think of a sentence and write it on a piece of paper.

2. Write the text backward, starting on the right side of the paper, and then flip the letters around. (Warning: this part is tricky. Good luck!)

Here's a mirror message from me to you.

Mathematicians love to work out how things are related to each other.

Are you receiving me?   YES   NO

I-SPY CROSSWORD

ACROSS

2. I rhyme with 'pie', 'eye' and 'my' (3)

3. sometimes, thieves leave these in the mud (10)

4. this may be a hat, a false nose and a wig (8)

5. lots of these help you solve a mystery (5)

7. observing someone's activities in a house or building nearby (8)

8. we use this to hide a message (6)   (for a clue to this clue, see pg 131)

DOWN

1. secretly listening to a conversation (13)

2. spying on other people (12)

6. the art of spying (9)

38   50   10   11

7   21   22   50

45   21   28   48

A **CIPHER** is a secret or disguised way of writing a message to keep it hidden. This is a popular way to send secret messages and there are many different kinds of ciphers.

50   14

33

34

A **TRANSPOSITION CIPHER** uses numbers. This 'transposes' one number directly onto another.

34

If your number was **26101949** and your key was **5**, this means you have to add 5 to each number.

46

Psst: Ignore tens if they appear when you add 5. When you encrypt 9, for example, and 9+5 = 14, replace the 9 with 4.

8

This kind of maths is called 'modular arithmetic' but its informal name is 'clock arithmetic' because it's related to how we add up times (e.g. 10:00 plus 5 hours becomes 3:00 because we subtract 12). The Caesar Cipher (see page 132) works in the same way because it is just like an analogue clock.

21

14   23

42   50

8   8   48

A Can you work out the encrypted number?

21

9   49   14   14

Your answer:

14

35   2   14

CaEsar cIpheR

The **Caesar Wheel** is one of the earliest and simplest of ciphers. It's one of my favourites.

The famous Roman ruler *Julius Caesar* used to write all his letters using this cipher so that's why it's named after him.

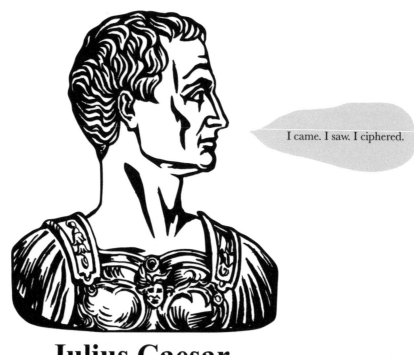

I came. I saw. I ciphered.

Julius Caesar

MAKE A CAESAR CIPHER

You will need

A photocopy of the two circles on the following pages (or you can trace them).

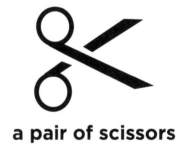

a pair of scissors

a brad pin

a marker

TRACE ME

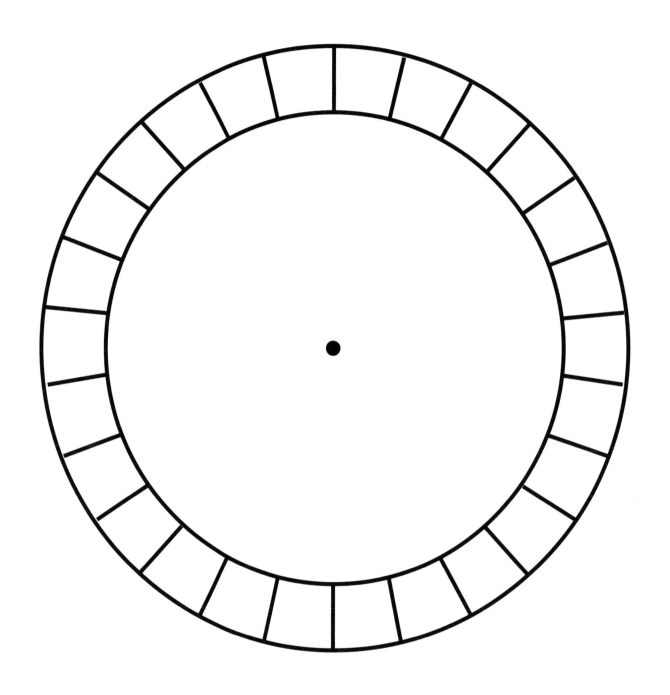

Big circle

TRACE ME

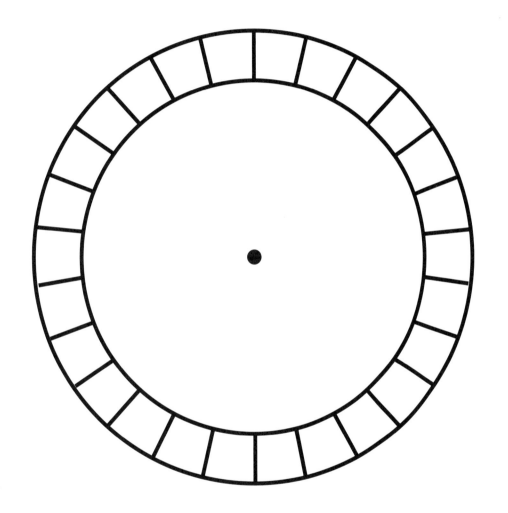

Small circle

1. In the big circle, write A–Z in the boxes around the outside. Follow a clockwise direction:

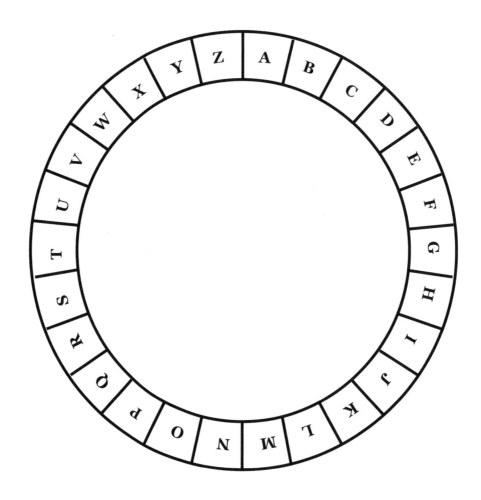

2. In the smaller circle, write a–z in the boxes around the outside in a clockwise direction:

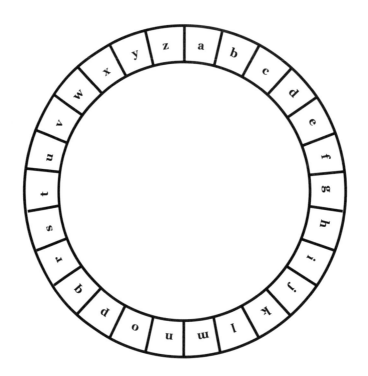

3. Cut out the two circles:

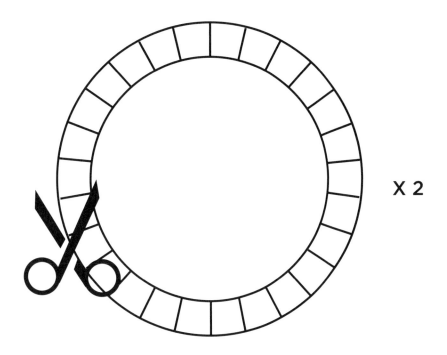

X 2

4. Make a hole through the dot in the centre of each circle:

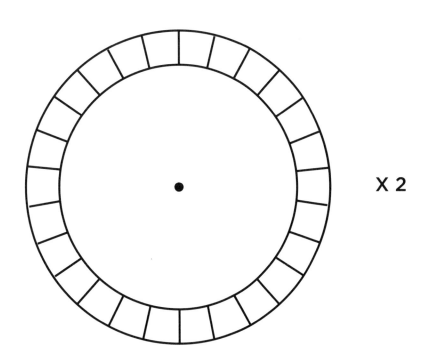

X 2

5. Place the small circle over the big circle, lining up the holes in the middle:

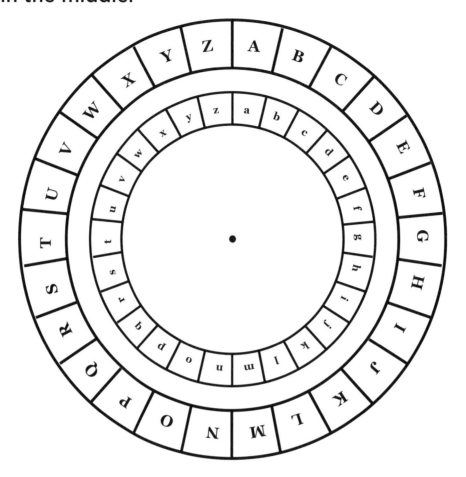

6. Join them together using a brad pin, some string or a paperclip:

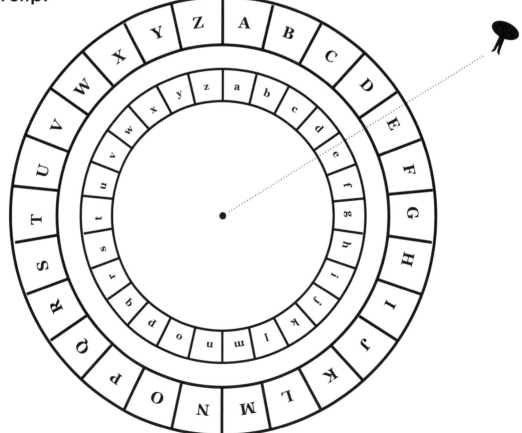

7. The two circles should now move around this centre hole. You are ready to go!

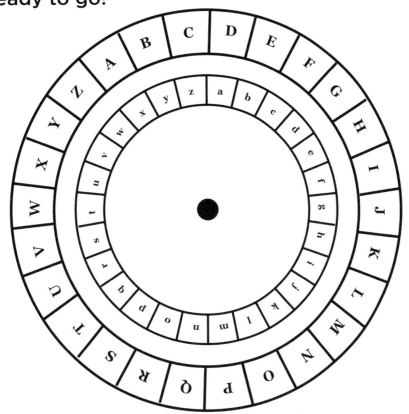

The Caesar Cipher works by shifting the letters in the alphabet (as shown by the big circle) along a certain number (as shown by the small circle).

For example, if you decided on a shift of 3 (this is your 'key' and you will need to share it with your friend so he or she can decode your message), A becomes x, B becomes y, C becomes z and so on.

Using a shift of 3, the word **MATHS** becomes: **JXQEP**.

Send a message to a friend using the Caesar Cipher.

OUTGOING

_____

_____

_____

Ask him or her to send you one back.

INCOMING

_____

_____

_____

ALPHABET SOUP

Did you know that the most common letter

in the alphabet is 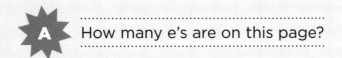?

There's nothing common about me!

The letter turns up in about 13% of most normal sentences in English.

A How many e's are on this page?

Your answer: _____

The second most common letter is **t**.

Second is not to be sneezed at!

A How many t's are on this page?

Your answer: _____

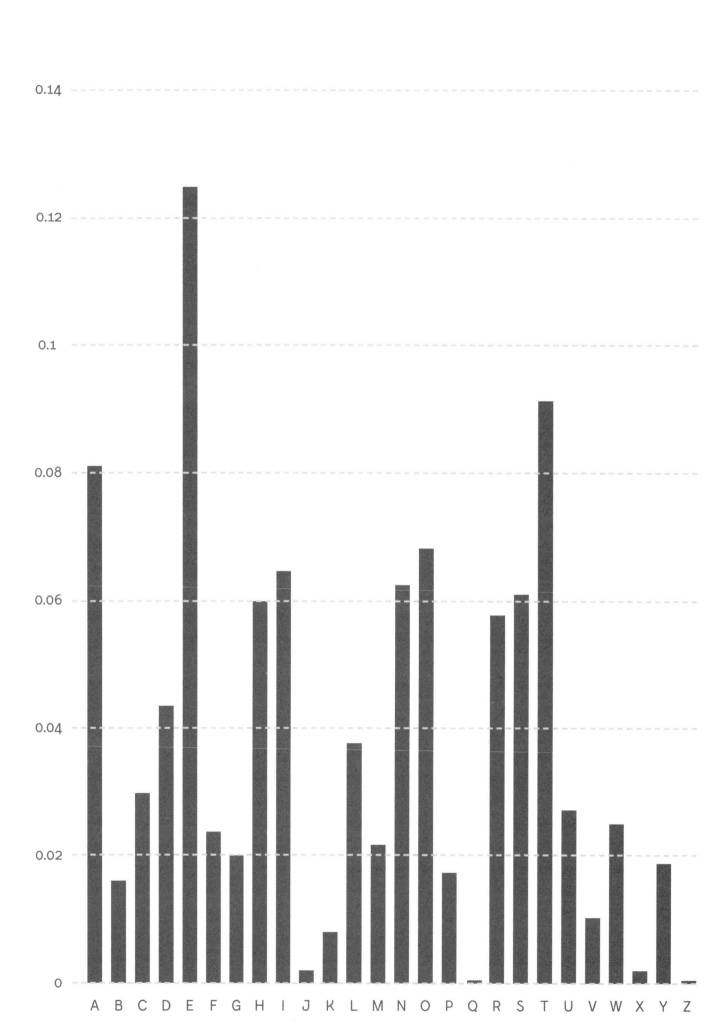

This graph shows you how often the letters of the alphabet are typically used in sentences. A graph like this is called a distribution. Each different language around the world has its own unique distribution, like a fingerprint!

If you write a long message, it is more likely to follow this distribution of the various letters. That means a cryptanalyst will be able to see patterns emerging and so crack your message.

Just remember this:

KEEP YOUR SECRET MESSAGE SHORT

bOOk cIpheR

A book cipher is an old-fashioned but excellent way to send messages using numbers.

The numbers are always in groups of three.

1. The first number is the page number.

2. The second number is the line number.

3. The third number refers to the position of the word in that line.

WHAT YOU NEED:

1. A copy of *Eddie Woo's Magical Maths 2*

2. A friend who either has a copy of *Eddie Woo's Magical Maths 2* or can share your copy.

3. A Top-Secret Message you need to tell your friend and you don't want anyone else to know.

ARE YOU READY TO CIPHER?   YES   NO

 Here is a secret message for you to decipher using this book.

Psst: Include the headings in your line count.

FOR YOUR EYES ONLY

19	3	8
61	12	2
86	7	1
102	6	4
32	4	9
68	3	2

BOOK CIPHER CLUB

Set up a Book Cipher Club with your friends,
or members of your family.

 First, you will need to fill out a **TOP SECRET SPY DOSSIER**
for each member of your club:

Psst: See page 148
to help you choose
a code name).

SECRET CODE NAME:

_____

AGE:

_____

HOBBIES:

_____

AVATAR:

_____

SPY SKILLS:

_____

MISSION:

_____

SECRET CODE NAME:

_____

AGE:

_____

HOBBIES:

_____

AVATAR:

_____

SPY SKILLS:

_____

MISSION:

_____

SECRET CODE NAME:

_____

AGE:

_____

HOBBIES:

_____

AVATAR:

_____

SPY SKILLS:

_____

MISSION:

_____

SECRET CODE NAME:

_____

AGE:

_____

HOBBIES:

_____

AVATAR:

_____

SPY SKILLS:

_____

MISSION:

_____

SECRET CODE NAME:

_____

AGE:

_____

HOBBIES:

_____

AVATAR:

_____

SPY SKILLS:

_____

MISSION:

_____

SECRET CODE NAME:

_____

AGE:

_____

HOBBIES:

_____

AVATAR:

_____

SPY SKILLS:

_____

MISSION:

_____

CoDe naMes

The Phonetic Alphabet is a great way to help you find a code name.

A	Alpha		N	November
B	Bravo		O	Oscar
C	Charlie		P	Papa
D	Delta		Q	Quebec
E	Echo		R	Romeo
F	Foxtrot		S	Sierra
G	Golf		T	Tango
H	Hotel		U	Uniform
I	India		V	Victor
J	Juliet		W	Whiskey
K	Kilo		X	X-ray
L	Lima		Y	Yankee
M	Mike		Z	Zulu

Work out what your initials become in the Phonetic Alphabet.

For example, my code name according to the Phonetic Alphabet is:

Echo Whiskey

Your code name:

_____

Your best friend's code name:

_____

Your mum's code name:

_____

Your dad's code name:

_____

Your sister's code name:

_____

Your brother's code name:

_____

Your favourite teacher's code name:

_____

Your pet's code name:

_____

ThE C0DEr

Nominate one member of your Book Cipher Club to be The Coder.

Ask him or her to write four messages using the Book Cipher or the Caesar Cipher for you to decode.

Compare your messages when you meet.

Top Secret Message 01:

_____

_____

_____

_____

_____

Top Secret Message 02:

_____

_____

_____

_____

Top Secret Message 03:

_____

_____

_____

_____

_____

Top Secret Message 04:

_____

_____

_____

_____

_____

A TRICK

OR TWO

THE 'DIFFERENCES' CARD TRICK

1. Using ten cards, Ace through to 10, divide the cards into two piles, then spread them out.

2. Each person lays out the cards and orders them from high to low, left to right (from their perspective).

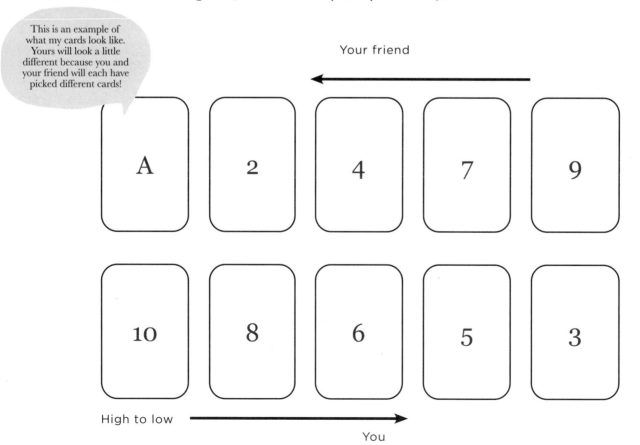

3. Calculate the differences between all the cards (ACE = 1).

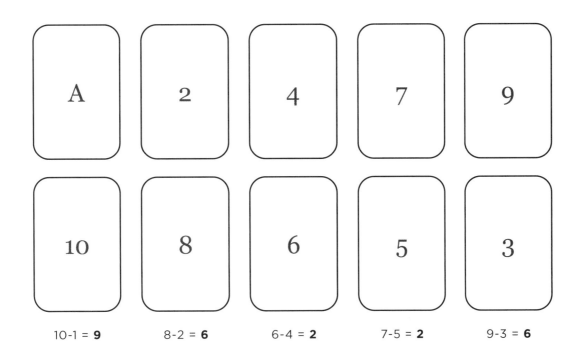

| 10-1 = **9** | 8-2 = **6** | 6-4 = **2** | 7-5 = **2** | 9-3 = **6** |

The sum of all the differences (in this case **9+6+2+2+6**)
is ***ALWAYS 25!***

BLACK HOLE

A competitive game for two players!

1. Begin by drawing a pyramid of 15 circles.

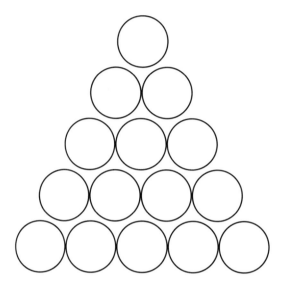

2. Each player chooses a place to write the number 1.

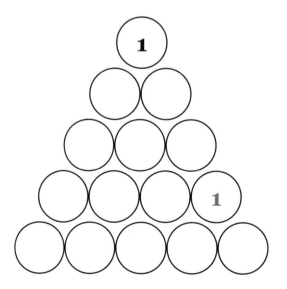

3. Each player continues writing 2, 3 and so on in order until both players write number 7.

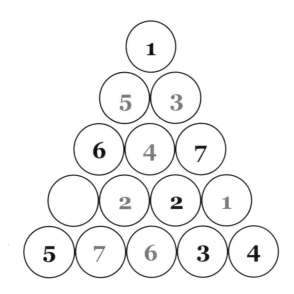

4. The final empty circle becomes the **BLACK HOLE**. It **EXPLODES**, taking all surrounding circles with it. Each player adds up their remaining circles. Whoever has the highest total **WINS!**

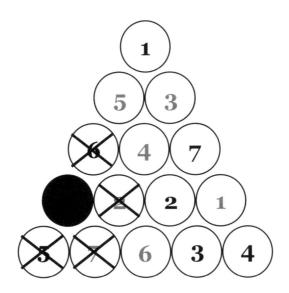

Player one: 1+7+2+3+4 = 17
Player two: 5+3+4+1+6 = 19

THE WINNER!

SPROUTS

A competitive game for two (or more) players!

1. On a blank piece of paper, draw some large dots – as many or as few as you like.

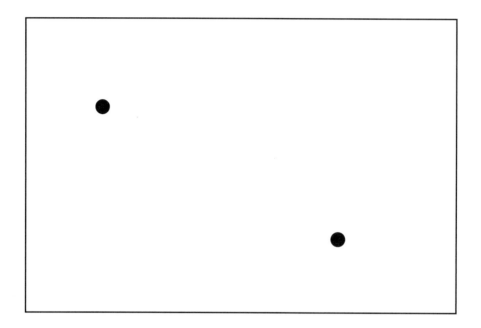

2. Each player takes turns joining the dots. Everytime you join two dots, they **SpRoUt** a new one.

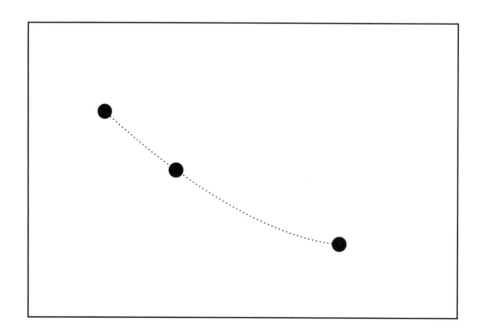

3. Each dot can have three lines coming out of it, but no more. When a dot reaches this point, it 'dies'.

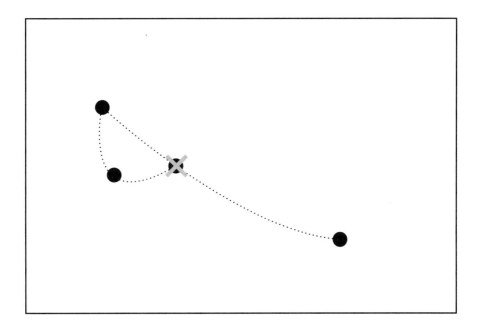

4. Dots can even join to themselves.

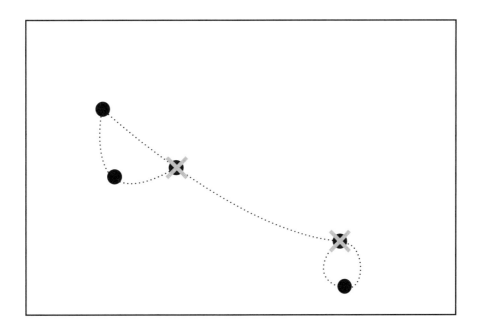

5. Lines can go anywhere . . . EXCEPT they aren't allowed to cross.

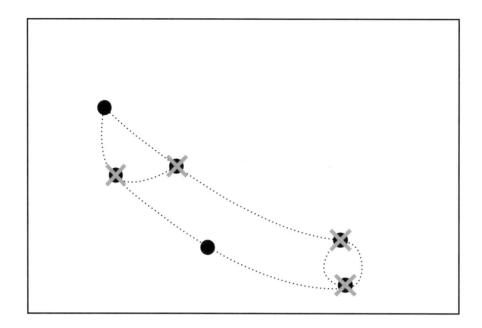

6. Eventually the game reaches a point were no more moves are possible. The last player to make a successful move *WINS!*

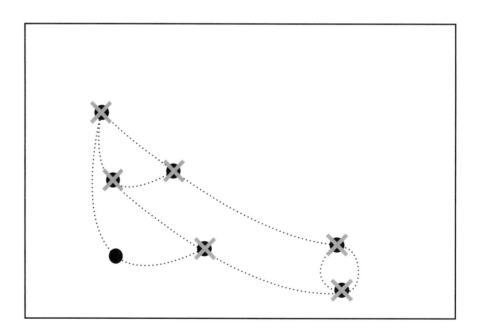

THE ANSWERS

PAGE XIV – BONUS QUESTION

What is the total tally of all the numbers mentioned on these two pages?

Answer = 47

Did you forget to include the **2** in EDDIE WOO'S MAGICAL MATHS **2**?

PAGE 5 – NUMBERS IN A NAME

Your answer: 159

```
W  E  R  B  T  Y  U  I  O  P  L  K  J  H  G  B
A  D  Q  M  O  N  B  V  C  X  Z  A  S  D  F  I
S  U  D  W  E  T  R  T  T  Y  D  U  B  F  O  N
L  P  U  P  C  Z  H  P  G  N  O  A  P  Q  V  A
Q  L  M  W  N  E  R  B  T  V  U  Y  D  S  U  R
N  E  D  J  T  Z  O  U  D  Q  B  X  K  A  E  Y
H  T  F  U  T  W  I  N  A  K  L  Z  V  N  D  O
P  S  I  Z  Q  L  F  S  C  B  E  R  D  U  A  L
E  L  K  R  N  A  J  A  O  P  F  B  G  Z  Q  J
H  A  L  V  E  K  Z  O  Q  W  R  T  E  T  Y  B
L  K  J  H  G  F  T  D  S  A  Z  X  C  V  N  M
E  D  C  R  F  V  T  G  B  Y  H  R  N  U  J  K
P  O  I  Y  U  T  J  Q  Z  O  I  A  C  K  A  T
K  E  D  U  O  G  A  S  W  A  L  P  E  O  Z  E
L  S  F  G  J  U  I  X  P  B  N  E  J  L  I  U
C  O  U  P  L  E  P  Q  L  A  S  D  F  G  H  D
```

PAGE 12 - SPEED TEST

Adding up as fast as you can:

7 + 6 = 13

20 + 5 = 25

31 + 6 = 37

8 + 22 = 30

46 + 4 = 50

18 + 15 = 33

32 + 32 = 64

19 + 3 = 22

64 + 5 = 69

124 + 123 = 247

Subtracting as fast as you can:

7 - 6 = 1

20 - 5 = 15

31 - 6 = 25

22 - 8 = 14

46 - 4 = 42

18 - 15 = 3

32 – 32 = 0

19 - 3 = 16

64 - 5 = 59

124 - 123 = 1

PAGE 15 - FILL IN THE MISSING SIMILES

As brave as a **lion**.

As boring as watching **paint** dry.

As cunning as a **fox**.

As cool as a **cucumber**.

As dead as a **doornail**.

As fresh as a **daisy**.

As loose as a **goose**.

As quiet as a **mouse.**

As regular as **clockwork**.

As sour as **vinegar**.

PAGE 16-17 - COUNT THE BUZZING BEES

There are **345** buzzing bees.

PAGE 19 - NUMBERS IN DISGUISE

fraction	decimal	percentage
¼	0.25	25%
½	0.5	50%
¾	0.75	75%
⅕	0.2	20%
⅖	0.4	40%
⅗	0.6	60%
⅘	0.8	80%
⅓	0.33	33.3%
⅔	0.66	66.66%

PAGE 22-23 – COLOUR IN THE FRACTIONS

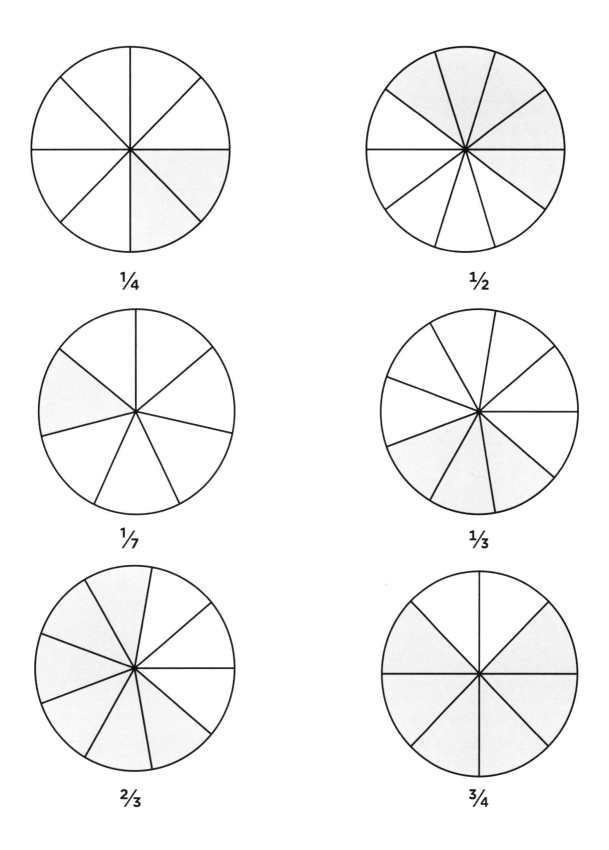

¼

½

⅐

⅓

⅔

¾

PAGE 22-23 – COLOUR IN THE FRACTIONS

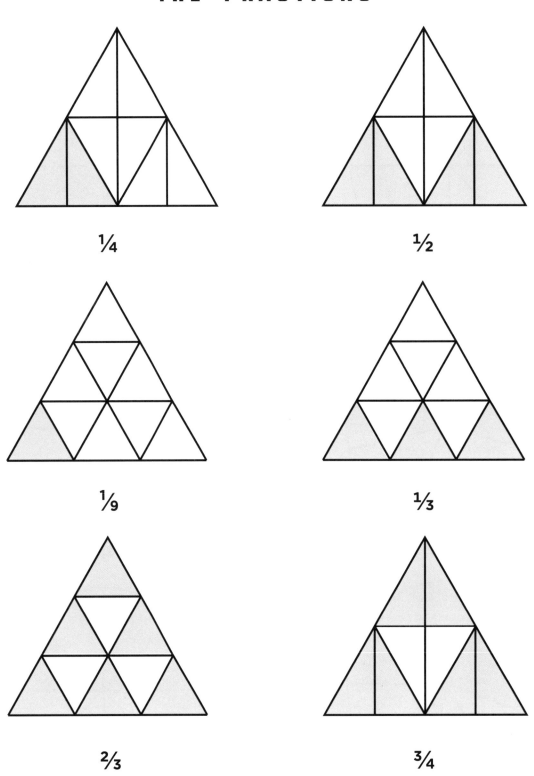

¼

½

⅑

⅓

⅔

¾

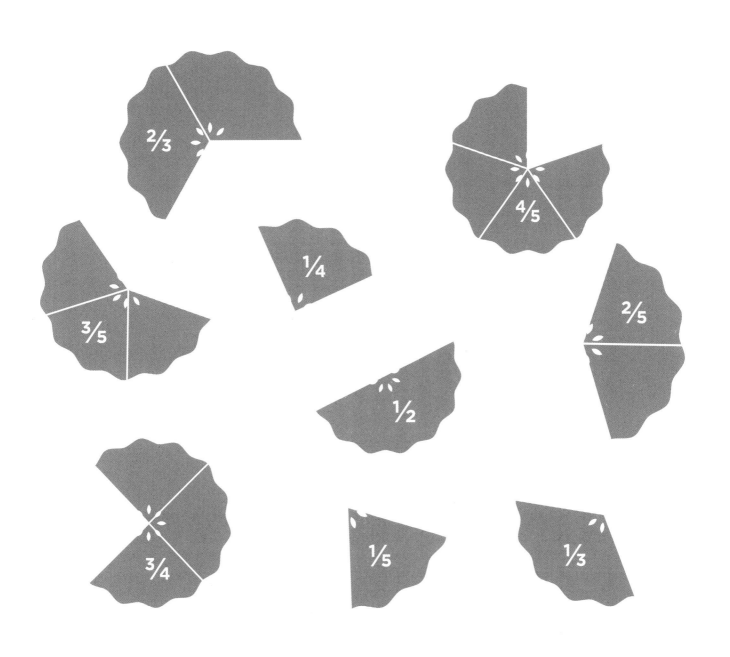

The number to the ⬅ of the point is the whole number.

So, in $19.25, the whole number is **19**.

The **first** number to the ➡ of the point is in the 'tenths' position.

So, in $19.25, the number in the tenths spot is **2**.

The **second** number to the ➡ of the point is in the 'hundredths' spot.

So, in $19.25, the number in the hundredths spot is **5**.

PAGE 35 - PERCENTAGES

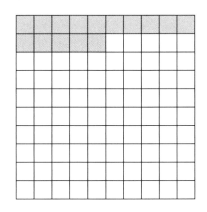

1. 15%

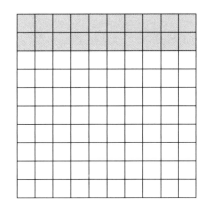

2. 20%

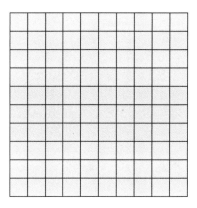

3. 100%

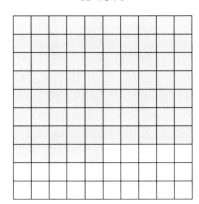

4. 75 %

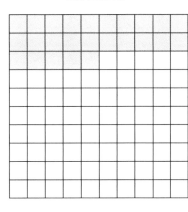

5. 25%

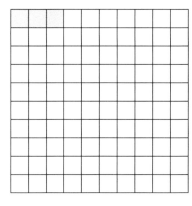

6. 3%

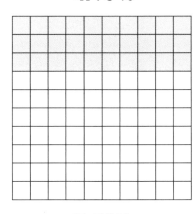

7. 30%

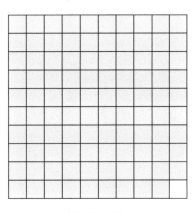

8. 99%

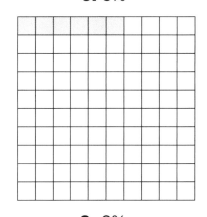

9. 6%

1. 85%

2. 80%

3. 0%

4. 25%

5. 75%

6. 97%

7. 70%

8. 1%

9. 94%

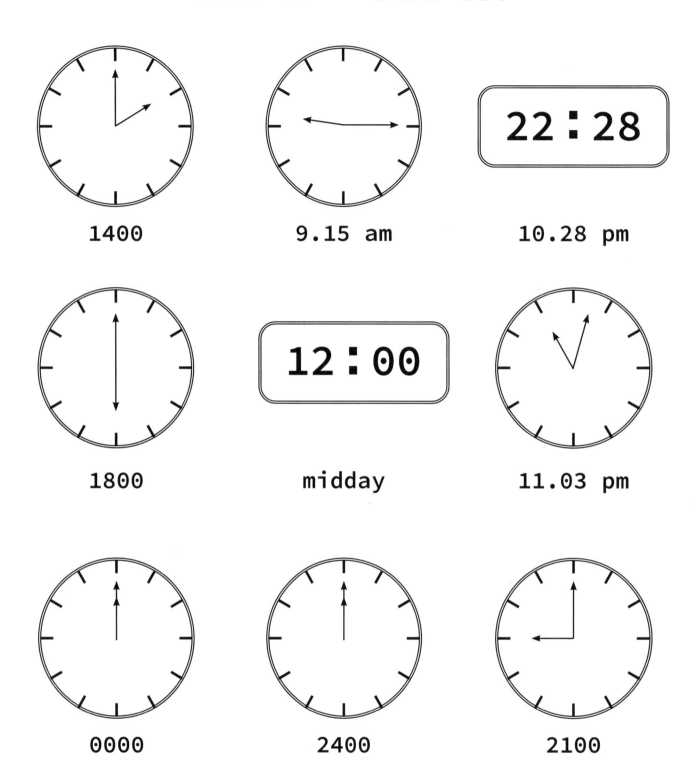

1400

9.15 am

22:28

1800

12:00

11.03 pm

0000

2400

2100

IT'S MATHS TIME

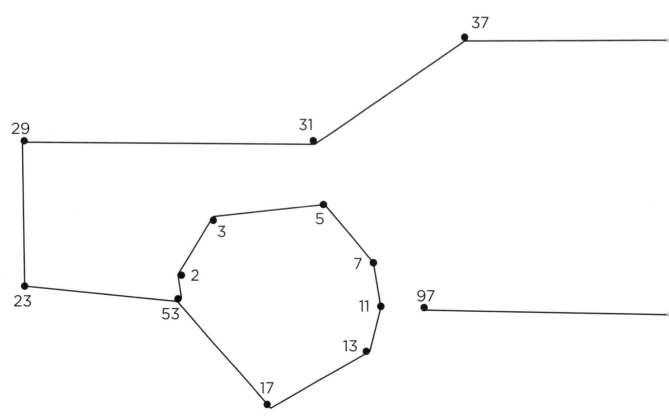

We ♥ limos

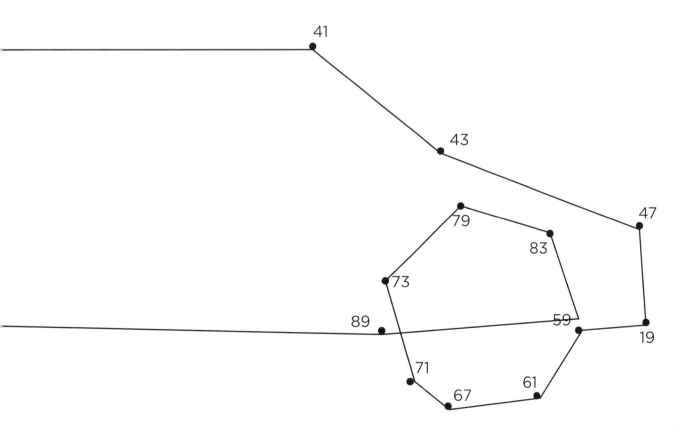

PAGE 54-55 - FUN WITH THE NUMBER ONE

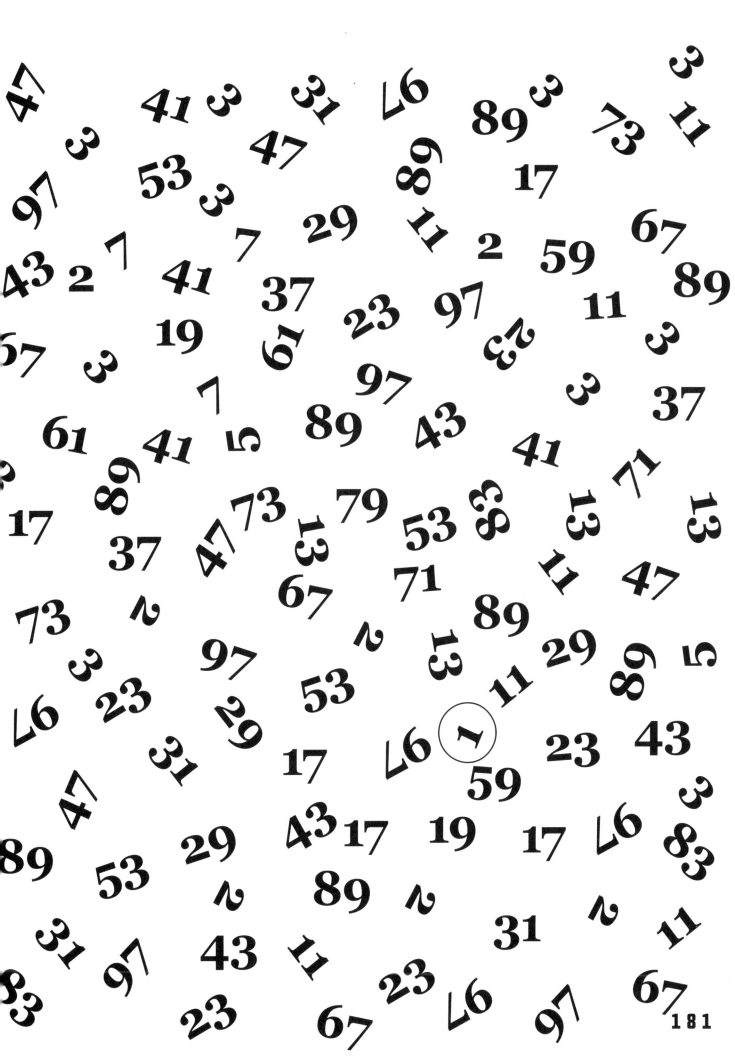

181

4	52	27	33	75	36	55	14	82	9	81	87	12	10	28	4	21	44	75	62
84	65	32	44	6	50	63	42	91	46	63	90	74	56	22	77	16	52	84	91
20	51	76	18	92	35	4	28	70	15	52	45	18	6	14	30	20	69	72	48
12	91	9	46	**PAGE 56-57 – COLOUR IN**										8	49	56	74	86	85
85	72	36	54	**THE PRIME NUMBERS**										51	34	15	58	70	81
63	14	81	6	30	56	10	65	82	9	16	27	25	38	63	65	9	24	36	55
32	52	2	21	87	4	21	6	80	15	22	52	4	62	56	32	75	92	40	98
45	81	90	46	99	28	76	24	35	50	45	60	12	8	91	66	84	8	54	95
12	26	15	8	14	33	40	10	42	57	68	76	25	21	80	45	39	76	82	56
22	4	10	63	27	18	34	54	26	63	74	90	6	46	88	93	85	55	4	75
9	25	56	74	9	20	49	70	56	90	87	85	91	10	94	26	42	68	99	57
27	80	21	32	16	91	25	82	8	75	86	10	18	27	62	72	90	9	63	70
6	14	55	44	28	45	72	38	64	15	36	9	49	22	58	92	69	44	73	29
52	62	87	50	12	55	69	90	77	27	96	93	76	33	75	64	71	5	3	61
20	76	35	66	72	24	84	51	93	68	87	45	98	82	50	67	23	11	17	67
40	58	7	30	80	65	46	76	74	91	4	84	77	13	79	53	47	13	73	31
64	16	29	61	42	33	81	92	8	88	85	48	2	43	11	29	19	5	71	5
75	51	39	13	5	73	70	87	38	66	57	52	29	61	53	31	67	43	97	23
26	85	95	53	23	83	17	45	63	34	5	79	11	53	67	17	79	59	61	13
92	60	24	56	41	47	59	31	67	97	71	47	3	31	13	23	41	17	3	53
48	81	65	72	54	3	11	43	2	11	83	53	67	23	59	97	5	31	67	29
12	52	57	46	63	42	58	37	19	61	19	31	17	71	43	83	7	11	19	97
27	68	30	82	78	6	21	50	4	13	23	59	29	67	11	2	47	73	83	5
8	45	70	87	60	92	45	88	65	24	51	38	53	73	7	97	53	89	23	67
51	66	84	91	55	16	33	76	80	12	77	10	67	17	43	19	13	59	17	29
34	22	81	75	48	26	57	54	22	68	62	49	14	59	3	41	23	61	47	13
15	62	56	86	39	64	93	16	40	35	24	27	6	83	79	89	7	2	16	52
54	36	72	10	87	9	86	28	9	56	84	69	58	5	47	29	11	97	40	74
50	69	4	78	80	77	44	12	6	70	92	75	30	86	65	55	82	78	56	4
25	58	65	32	46	52	90	74	82	21	63	18	42	91	48	60	76	81	25	33

56	68	88	6	45	38	50	26	70	62	85	54	9	80	93	57	65	22	49	35
82	50	63	4	33	14	28	82	66	42	36	69	39	25	76	10	91	78	6	58
58	34	70	80	54	64	46	33	74	51	2	7	97	60	27	85	34	55	40	20
77	92	46	65	26	49	24	57	21	3	89	71	37	23	30	45	68	52	32	75
55	69	52	91	39	6	68	81	44	11	5	89	13	19	47	53	16	76	84	99
62	36	90	8	86	35	75	25	9	59	43	3	97	73	41	61	23	46	72	88
72	48	66	4	30	63	56	80	48	10	61	2	17	43	13	5	29	38	91	14
81	57	78	16	58	16	58	36	52	68	23	67	79	66	51	8	96	9	82	56
65	4	85	74	21	46	72	22	76	4	37	97	31	76	28	12	62	69	12	33
50	75	22	87	35	42	69	45	55	30	41	17	5	32	70	54	24	87	44	90
64	46	60	12	68	8	24	60	78	12	53	11	71	15	36	4	22	65	92	8
27	63	82	42	76	20	32	54	26	66	19	83	47	9	63	48	74	16	35	10
5	2	28	93	55	38	51	70	62	13	2	59	82	56	82	99	86	26	95	78
31	37	83	6	24	27	65	18	64	3	97	61	25	90	49	24	15	93	18	64
83	5	17	37	41	44	34	74	6	19	43	5	72	69	91	98	75	62	55	30
67	89	19	71	19	7	48	40	79	31	61	37	46	94	27	76	36	4	18	74
43	73	47	3	43	5	9	32	53	11	89	41	82	50	16	39	14	72	33	6
31	19	2	11	67	2	59	41	83	29	17	7	32	75	6	10	52	99	51	66
5	59	89	97	17	89	29	3	97	73	41	61	8	99	51	74	20	40	70	88
83	2	23	19	3	53	7	19	61	2	13	83	26	42	76	16	28	32	21	9
37	53	79	83	29	67	41	29	17	67	11	60	93	34	84	9	81	46	65	15
97	61	5	7	19	11	13	83	73	59	43	18	64	90	78	62	10	75	92	21
47	83	11	2	67	53	2	23	5	13	49	28	80	98	44	95	72	68	26	86
2	89	17	59	19	37	41	61	7	20	58	63	92	22	87	21	14	94	12	74
37	53	29	3	41	89	17	59	21	35	72	46	85	66	14	6	25	42	80	96
19	5	97	13	31	43	9	52	74	57	78	88	91	38	57	98	64	85	99	51
32	47	83	29	53	11	24	39	15	4	75	30	24	96	69	40	6	10	84	36
21	13	2	37	79	5	28	70	62	81	55	76	95	74	78	92	48	27	93	46
77	54	10	63	44	12	32	51	45	68	84	33	86	60	22	54	90	35	58	70
14	38	57	72	18	26	48	36	10	56	65	42	8	16	82	63	75	50	4	39

PAGE 61 - PRIME SUSPECT
BONUS QUESTION

Add up all the numbers mentioned on this page.

My answer is: 62

PAGE 62-63 - SUSPECT LINE-UP

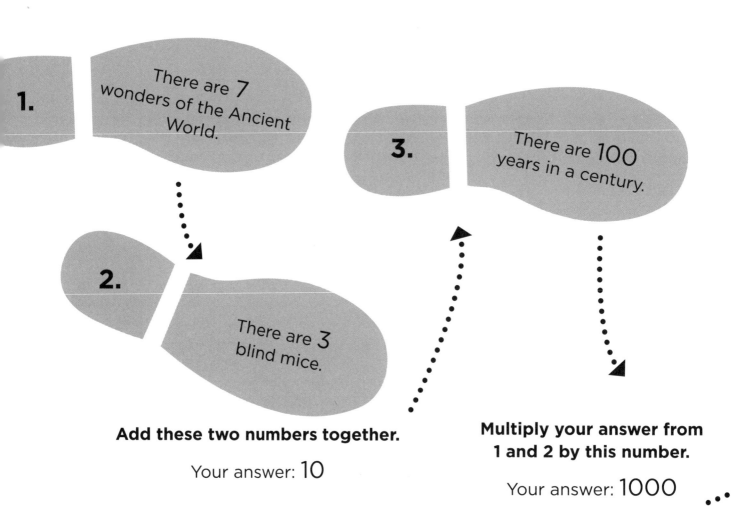

1.

There are 7 wonders of the Ancient World.

2.

There are 3 blind mice.

Add these two numbers together.

Your answer: 10

3.

There are 100 years in a century.

Multiply your answer from 1 and 2 by this number.

Your answer: 1000

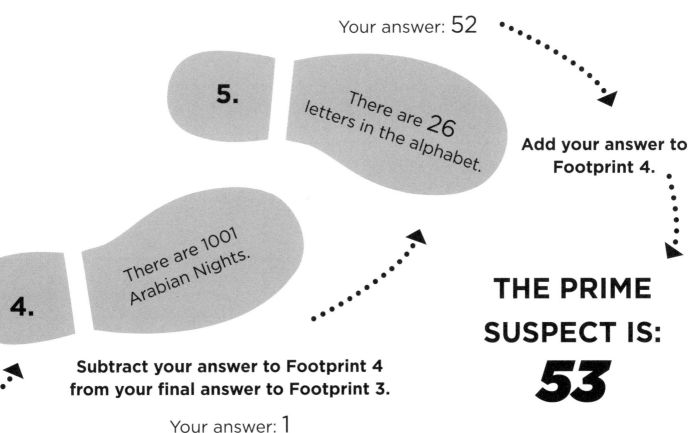

Multiply your answer to Footprint 5 by two.

Your answer: 52

5.

There are 26 letters in the alphabet.

Add your answer to Footprint 4.

THE PRIME SUSPECT IS:

53

There are 1001 Arabian Nights.

4.

Subtract your answer to Footprint 4 from your final answer to Footprint 3.

Your answer: 1

PAGE 73 – FINDING OUT ABOUT FACTALS

leaf

tree

blood vessels

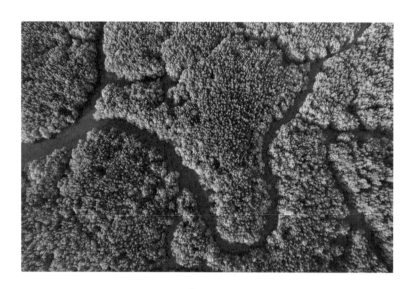

rivers

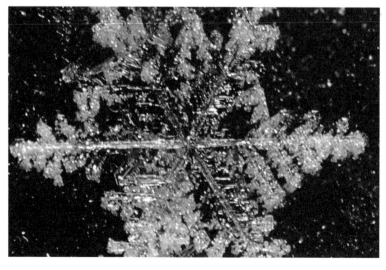

snowflake

shell

sunflower

staircase

broccoli

fingerprint

PAGE 101 - LOOKING AT THE LUNG
BONUS QUESTION

If we take 20,000 breaths a day, how many breaths would
we take in:

a) a week   **140,000**
b) a 30-day month   **600,000**
c) a year   **7,300,000**

PAGE 103 - INGENIOUS WORDS

1. genius

2. one

3. snug

4. noise

5. nouns

6. sung

7. son

8. gone

9. nine

10. nose

There are so many more words, like NEON, GENUS and USING.
How many more were you able to come up with?

_____

Your answer: **A sponge**

PAGE 105 - ANIMAL BRAINS

sperm whale	5 kg
elephant	1.7 kg
human	8 kg
killer whale	6 kg
dolphin	1.5 kg
blue whale	6 kg
Triceratops	0.097 kg
goldfish	7 kg

BONUS QUESTION

I am a **leech**.

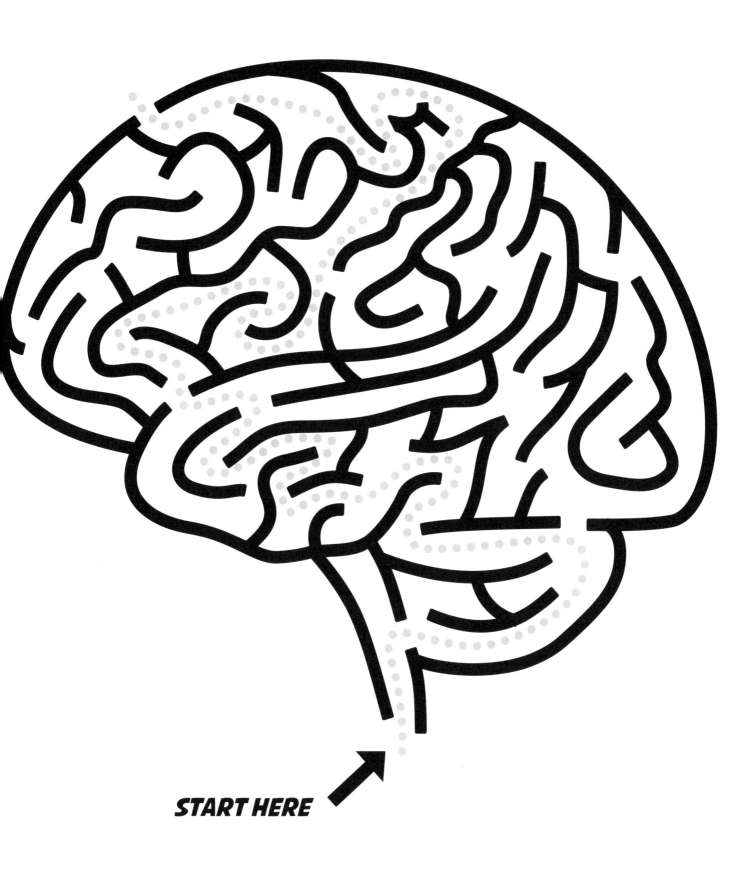

START HERE

PAGE 116 - HERE ARE SOME OF MY FAVOURITE QUIET WORDS

hushed

soundless

tranquil

quiesce

serene

PAGE 117 - QUIET WORDS

angry

balloons

serene

soft

marshmallow

razzle-dazzle

hushed

scream

swim

still

voiceless

noisy

ice cream

doughnut

gentle

loud

deafening

wild

roaring

broccoli

sombre

yellow

low

screaming

clouds

polka dot

howling

zoo

sleep

pizza

boisterous

shampoo

speechless

agitated

shrill

spaghetti

clamorous

197

Mathematicians love to work out how things are related to each other.

PAGE 128-129 - I-SPY CROSSWORD

1. eavesdropping
2. spy
3. footprints
4. disguise
5. clues
6. e
7. stakeout
8. cipher

surveillance

espionage

PAGE 131 - CODES NEED KEYS

My answer is: **71656494**

PAGE 141 - HOW MANY E'S ARE ON THIS PAGE?

My answer is: 33

PAGE 141 - HOW MANY T'S ARE ON THIS PAGE?

My answer is: 29

PAGE 145 - THE SECRET CIPHER MESSAGE IS:

The universe is full of patterns

SOME CARD TRICK TIPS:

Try this trick a few ways. What patterns do you notice?

If we call the cards Ace, 2, 3, 4 and 5 the 'low cards' and then call the 6, 7, 8, 9 and 10 the 'high cards', do you notice that we never subtract a low card from a low card (or a high card from a high card)? Why do you think this happens?

What do all the low cards add up to?

What do all the high card add up to?

When you figure out how the trick works, try and come up with your own version where the total is something other than 25!

WANT MORE MATHS?

EDDIE WOO'S MAGICAL MATHS

colour & count

puzzles & patterns

games galore

draw & doodle

make a snowflake

shape up

fun maths activities for kids

THE

END